IF SOMETHING HAPPENS TO ME®

A WORKBOOK TO HELP ORGANIZE YOUR FINANCIAL AND LEGAL AFFAIRS

Joseph R. Hearn

and

Niel D. Nielsen

PROVISION · PLANNING · FORESIGHT

Important Reminder

This workbook is designed to provide accurate and authoritative information in regard to the subject matter covered. It is sold with the understanding that neither the authors nor the publisher is engaged in rendering legal, accounting, financial, or other professional advice or services. If legal advice or other expert assistance is required, you should seek the services of a competent professional.

Provisio Publishing, LLC
11104 John Galt Blvd.
Omaha, NE 68137
www.provisiopublishing.com

Copyright © 2004 Provisio Publishing, LLC

Edited by Bruce Arant and Rob Taylor
Art Design and Layout by Jeff Dedlow
Proofread by Fran Wacht

Printed and bound in the United States of America

Library of Congress Cataloging-in-Publication Data Available

04 05 06 07 08 09 10

ISBN: 0-9760265-0-3

To our wives, Margie and Julie

"A wife of noble character who can find?
She is worth far more than rubies."

–Proverbs 31:10

Do you know anyone who could use this book?

Go to www.ifsomethinghappenstome.com and click on "Tell a Friend."
The book also makes a great gift. Just click on "Order Now" at our
website, and we will send a copy along with a personalized note to
your friend or loved one.

In addition, if your group or organization would like to go through the
book together, or you would like to order multiple copies to give away,
we offer special discounts when you order more than one. Just visit
www.ifsomethinghappenstome.com and click on "Order Now."

Contents

Contents

Part B - Administering the Estate

Part C - Applying for Government Benefits

Section 7- Safe-Deposit Box Storage

Section 8 - Document Locator System

Section 9- Annual Review Checklist

Section 10- Notes

Introduction

For most of us, organizing our financial and legal affairs is not a high priority. We all have busy lives to lead, and setting our affairs in order just doesn't seem very urgent. Life can change suddenly, however, and when it does, our planning and preparation will become vitally important.

As a financial adviser and an estate planning attorney, we recognize the struggle between enjoying life today and planning for the future. We designed *If Something Happens to Me* to help you accomplish both. The workbook is written in a clear and comprehensive format, and by completing it, you will gain three valuable benefits for your family:

1) Save your hard-earned money.

Attorneys, accountants, and financial advisers charge thousands of dollars to organize our estates when we die. Part of these expenses simply involves time spent tracking down records of what we own, what we owe, who is in charge, and who should receive our property. By completing this workbook beforehand, you can save a portion of that money for your family because they won't have to pay your advisers for hours of wading through your records.

2) Save those you love a lot of grief.

Losing you would be tough on your family. Sadly, the pain, stress, aggravation, family quarrels, lost time, and wasted money that result from poor planning and organization only multiply the pain. Completing this workbook will help you clearly communicate your wishes to your family, lay out a roadmap of the steps you want them to take, and list trusted friends and advisers to provide help and advice. Putting your affairs in order now will not only simplify things for your family, it will clearly express to them how much you love them.

3) Avoid legal and financial pitfalls.

We all can't be experts at everything. The wisest people are those that avoid mistakes by knowing when to seek advice. We have helped hundreds of families put the many pieces of their financial and legal planning in order. The knowledge and experience we have in these matters is built into this workbook, and they are intended to help you succeed in your planning and make smart decisions for your family.

By investing a small amount of time and energy in this workbook, you can ensure a great savings in time, hassle, and expense. We want your plans to succeed, and hope this book will help you leave a positive legacy for your family.

Joseph R. Hearn

Niel D. Nielsen

Preface
How To Use This Workbook

This workbook is organized into 10 sections, each with its own professional guidance, forms, tips, and instructions. By following our guidance and completing this workbook, you will go a long way toward ensuring that your financial and legal affairs are in order. Upon completing it, you will have peace of mind, knowing that should something happen to you or your spouse, the other will be able to simply reference this book to find an obituary, life insurance details, account numbers, pension information, safe-deposit box information, will/trust information, and countless other details.

There are two types of people that will use this workbook. We call them the Primary Users and the Secondary Users. The Primary Users are those that are using this workbook as a tool to organize their financial and estate planning information. The Secondary Users are those who, after losing a spouse or loved one, are using this workbook as an informational resource to handle their financial and legal affairs.

If you are a Primary User:

- Fill out this workbook as completely as possible. It is probably a good idea to write in pencil, so you can make updates if any of the information changes.

- Use this workbook as a checklist to complete your financial and estate planning. For example, if you get to the long-term care insurance section and do not have that type of coverage, take the opportunity to speak with your financial adviser to see if you should.

- If you are married, complete the workbook with your spouse.

- If you are married, make sure that your spouse knows where this workbook will be kept. If you are single, make sure the person you have chosen to handle your affairs in the event of your death knows where this workbook is located.

- Review and make updates to this workbook at least once a year.

If you are a Secondary User:

- Begin in Section 6. It includes a checklist for everything that needs to be done and it references every other section in the book.

- Work closely with the list of advisers beginning on page 15. They will be able to discuss the different options available to you and offer expert advice.

- Update any changes to information as you go. By doing so, whomever you choose to handle your affairs in the event of your death will have all the information necessary.

Visit Us On The Web At
www.ifsomethinghappenstome.com

- Obtain a Document Organizer for your important documents.
- Buy copies of the workbook for friends or relatives.
- Buy a CD-Rom that contains electronic copies of each form found in the book.

Section I
Personal Information

This first section is fairly straightforward and should be easy for you to complete. By completing it fully, you will have provided a valuable resource for those involved in handling your affairs. In this section:

- ☐ Personal Information
- ☐ Contact Information
- ☐ Children and Other Dependents
- ☐ Employer Information
- ☐ Professional Advisers

Personal Information

Full name(s)	Date of birth	Social Security number
①		
②		

Contact Information

address		
home phone	cell	fax
email		
email	cell	fax

Children and Other Dependents

Full name	Date of birth	Social Security number
address		
home phone	cell	fax
email		

Full name	Date of birth	Social Security number
address		
home phone	cell	fax
email		

Full name	Date of birth	Social Security number
address		
home phone	cell	fax
email		

www.ifsomethinghappenstome.com

Full name	Date of birth	Social Security number

address

home phone	cell	fax

email

Full name	Date of birth	Social Security number

address

home phone	cell	fax

email

Full name	Date of birth	Social Security number

address

home phone	cell	fax

email

Full name	Date of birth	Social Security number

address

home phone	cell	fax

email

Employer Information

My employer   **Position held**

address

office phone	cell	fax

email

notes

My employer   **Position held**

address

office phone	cell	fax

email

notes

My spouse's employer   **Position held**

address

office phone	cell	fax

email

notes

My spouse's employer   **Position held**

address

office phone	cell	fax

email

notes

Professional Advisers

Note: Additional advisers in each of these categories can be listed, beginning on page 18.

My financial adviser's name	Firm or company name
address	
office phone	cell	fax
email	
notes	

My attorney's name	Firm or company name
address	
office phone	cell	fax
email	
notes	

My accountant's name

Firm or company name

address

office phone

cell

fax

email

notes

My insurance agent's name

Firm or company name

address

office phone

cell

fax

email

notes

My banker's name

Firm or company name

address	
office phone	cell	fax
email	
notes	

My physician's name

Firm or company name

address	
office phone	cell	fax
email	
notes	

Below is space for additional advisers you may have.
For example, you may have more than one attorney, or you
may want to list your clergy, real estate agent, or other adviser.

Adviser's name	Firm or company name
address	
office phone	cell	fax
email	
notes	

Adviser's name	Firm or company name
address	
office phone	cell	fax
email	
notes	

www.ifsomethinghappenstome.com

Adviser's name

Firm or company name

address

office phone   cell   fax

email

notes

Adviser's name

Firm or company name

address

office phone   cell   fax

email

notes

Section 2
Financial Information: Assets & Liabilities

As you might imagine, knowing what you have is an important aspect of your planning. Your attorney uses this information to create your estate plan. Your financial adviser uses it to create your financial plan. You and your spouse use it to keep track of the progress you are making toward your financial goals. This section will help you to make a detailed listing of your financial affairs.

In this section:

Part A - Assets

- ☐ Bank Accounts
- ☐ Brokerage Accounts
- ☐ Individual Retirement Accounts
- ☐ Employer-Sponsored Plans
- ☐ Pensions
- ☐ Annuities
- ☐ Education Savings Accounts
- ☐ Real Estate
- ☐ Closely Held Business
- ☐ Automobiles and Other Vehicles
- ☐ Tangible Personal Property
- ☐ Miscellaneous Assets
- ☐ Summary of Assets

Part B - Liabilities

- ☐ Mortgage Information
- ☐ Vehicle Debt
- ☐ Credit Card Information
- ☐ Student Loans
- ☐ Personal Loans/Lines of Credit
- ☐ Business Loans/Lines of Credit
- ☐ Summary of Liabilities

"My husband handled our finanaces and he was always very organized. After being diagnosed with cancer, he spent time with me going over our investments, life insurance, and wills. Although losing him was extremely difficult, his thoughtful pre-planning alleviated a significant burden from me and our children."

Margaret T.

PLANNING INSIGHT At its most basic level, financial planning is simply coming up with answers to three questions regarding your finances. Those are: 1) Where am I? 2) Where do I want to be? 3) How am I going to get there? Your financial adviser can help answer these questions and make sure you are on track to meet your financial goals.

Bank Accounts

It is important to have a portion of your assets liquid in order to pay bills, cover your day-to-day expenses, and meet any emergencies that may arise. Most people accomplish this by having both a checking and savings account. There are typically few restrictions on accessing your money, and the Federal Deposit Insurance Corporation insures your accounts up to $100,000 per account. Checking accounts typically do not pay interest, so most people keep only enough in the account to cover their regular monthly bills, while they use an interest-bearing savings account to temporarily park money that is used to pay bills that come due less frequently (for example, house taxes, car taxes, insurance, etc.). Record the information regarding your checking and savings accounts below.

Institution	Account number	Owner(s)	Current value

tax I.D. number		type of account	☐ Checking ☐ Money Market ☐ Other: ☐ Savings ☐ C.D.
signer(s)		P.O.D. designation*	
notes and locations of records			

Institution	Account number	Owner(s)	Current value

tax I.D. number		type of account	☐ Checking ☐ Money Market ☐ Other: ☐ Savings ☐ C.D.
signer(s)		P.O.D. designation*	
notes and locations of records			

*P.O.D. and T.O.D. refer to Payable on Death and Transfer on Death, respectively. This is an account designation used to transfer an account to another person in the event of your death.

Institution	Account number	Owner(s)	Current value

tax I.D. number		type of account	☐ Checking ☐ Money Market ☐ Other:
			☐ Savings ☐ C.D.

signer(s)	P.O.D. designation*

notes and locations of records	

Institution	Account number	Owner(s)	Current value

tax I.D. number		type of account	☐ Checking ☐ Money Market ☐ Other:
			☐ Savings ☐ C.D.

signer(s)	P.O.D. designation*

notes and locations of records	

Total value of my bank accounts	$

Brokerage Accounts

For our purposes, we will describe "brokerage accounts" as non-retirement investment accounts held at a financial institution (for example, a brokerage firm, bank, or mutual fund). More specifically, these would be your non-retirement accounts containing stocks, bonds and mutual funds. Since retirement accounts like IRAs and 401(k)s have specific tax benefits, Congress has limited the amount of money that you may contribute to those plans in any given year, and you may access that money only under certain circumstances. For this reason, people will often establish other investment accounts once they have maximized their contributions to their retirement accounts. Record below the details relating to your brokerage accounts.

Institution	Account number	Owner(s)	Current value
account representative		taxpayer I.D.	
type of account ☐ Individual ☐ Tenants in common ☐ Joint tenant with right of survivorship		T.O.D. designation*	
notes and locations of records			

Institution	Account number	Owner(s)	Current value
account representative		taxpayer I.D.	
type of account ☐ Individual ☐ Tenants in common ☐ Joint tenant with right of survivorship		T.O.D. designation*	
notes and locations of records			

*P.O.D. and T.O.D. refer to Payable on Death and Transfer on Death, respectively. This is an account designation used to transfer an account to another person in the event of your death.

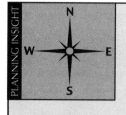

PLANNING INSIGHT

For tax purposes, it is important to keep track of your original cost basis, as well as information regarding any dividends or capital gains paid on your investments. Dividends are often paid quarterly and it would be impractical to try to record that information here. A better way to keep track of dividends would be to retain your year-end statements, which should contain a record of all activity in the account for the previous year. If you don't have the statements, you can often call the firm that is holding the account and ask for a history of the account.

Institution	Account number	Owner(s)	Current value

account representative		taxpayer I.D.

type of account	☐ Individual ☐ Tenants in common	T.O.D. designation*
	☐ Joint tenant with right of survivorship	

notes and locations of records

Institution	Account number	Owner(s)	Current value

account representative		taxpayer I.D.

type of account	☐ Individual ☐ Tenants in common	T.O.D. designation*
	☐ Joint tenant with right of survivorship	

notes and locations of records

Total value of my brokerage accounts	$

Individual Retirement Accounts (IRAs)

The IRA is an account used to accumulate money for retirement in which your investments grow tax-deferred. There are two types of IRAs: a) Traditional, and b) Roth. If you are eligible, the Traditional allows you to take a tax deduction on all or part of your contribution. With the Traditional, your investments grow tax-deferred until you withdraw them, at which time they are taxed. There are no tax deductions allowed on contributions to a Roth IRA, but when you withdraw the money at retirement, it generally will not be taxed. Because of the back end tax benefits, the Roth is especially attractive to those investors with long-term time horizons. There are certain income requirements that dictate whether you are eligible for a Roth, and whether you may deduct a Traditional IRA contribution. Speak with your financial adviser to see how this applies to you. The table below provides a summary of IRAs. Because Congress periodically makes changes to the rules governing retirement accounts, you should speak with your financial adviser to obtain the most current information available.

	Roth IRA	Traditional IRA
What is it?	The Roth IRA allows you to save for retirement with after-tax dollars. Your investments grow tax-deferred, and qualified withdrawals are generally not taxed.	The Traditional IRA also allows you to save for retirement, and you may be eligible to take a tax deduction on your contributions. Your investments grow tax-deferred until you withdraw them, at which time they are taxed.
Tax-deferred growth?	Yes	Yes
Tax-deductible contributions?	No	Maybe. Speak to your financial adviser.
Taxable withdrawals?	Generally not	Yes

The government limits the amount of money that you may contribute to IRAs. In addition, it allows a catch-up provision for people who reach age 50 or older by the end of the year in which the contribution is made. The table below contains a summary of the contribution limits.

IRA and Roth IRA contribution limits		
Year	Maximum contribution*	Maximum contribution plus catch-up provision
2004	$3000	$3500
2005	$4000	$4500
2006	$4000	$5000
2007	$4000	$5000
2008	$5000	$6000

*After 2008, contribution limits will be adjusted for inflation in $500 increments.

www.ifsomethinghappenstome.com

Record the information regarding your Traditional and Roth IRAs below.

Institution	Account number	Owner	Current value

account representative		type of account	☐ Traditional IRA ☐ Other: ☐ Roth IRA

taxpayer I.D.	primary beneficiary	contingent beneficiary

notes and locations of records

Institution	Account number	Owner	Current value

account representative		type of account	☐ Traditional IRA ☐ Other: ☐ Roth IRA

taxpayer I.D.	primary beneficiary	contingent beneficiary

notes and locations of records

Institution	Account number	Owner	Current value

account representative		type of account	☐ Traditional IRA ☐ Other: ☐ Roth IRA

taxpayer I.D.	primary beneficiary	contingent beneficiary

notes and locations of records

Institution	Account number	Owner	Current value

account representative		type of account	☐ Traditional IRA ☐ Other: ☐ Roth IRA

taxpayer I.D.	primary beneficiary	contingent beneficiary

notes and locations of records

Institution	Account number	Owner	Current value

account representative		type of account	☐ Traditional IRA ☐ Other: ☐ Roth IRA

taxpayer I.D.	primary beneficiary	contingent beneficiary

notes and locations of records

Institution	Account number	Owner	Current value

account representative		type of account	☐ Traditional IRA ☐ Other: ☐ Roth IRA

taxpayer I.D.	primary beneficiary	contingent beneficiary

notes and locations of records

Total value of my IRA accounts	$

Employer-Sponsored Plans
401(k)s, 403(b)s, 457 Plans, and Simple IRAs

Employer-sponsored retirement plans are a good way for employers to reward and retain employees while helping them to accumulate money for retirement. Contributions are generally made based on your pre-tax income, which simply means that you pay yourself before you pay the government. In addition, employers will often match a certain percentage of the contributions that you make. The investments in these accounts grow tax-deferred and are taxed only when withdrawn. These are excellent savings vehicles, not only for the tax benefits and employer match, but also because the contributions are automatically removed from your check by your employer. This acts as a kind of forced savings plan. As with IRAs, there are limits on the amount of money you may contribute to these types of plans. The limits are outlined in the table below. As mentioned before, Congress periodically makes changes to the laws governing retirement accounts, so you should speak with your adviser to obtain the most current information available.

Contribution limits for 401(k)s, 403(b)s, and 457 Plans		
Year	Maximum contribution*	Maximum contribution plus catch-up provision
2006	$15,000	$20,000
2007	$15,500	$20,500
2008	$15,500	$20,500

Contribution limits for Simple IRAs		
Year	Maximum contribution*	Maximum contribution plus catch-up provision
2006	$10,000	$12,500
2007	$10,500	$13,000
2008	$10,500	$13,000

*After 2008, contribution limits will be adjusted for inflation in $500 increments.

If you leave your job, it is often a good idea to take your company-sponsored retirement plan with you. You have several options for doing this. If the plan at your new employer allows, you could transfer the money from your old plan to your new one. Another option is to "rollover" the money into an IRA in your name. The worst option would be to have your company pay the money directly to you because you will be taxed on it and have to pay a 10% penalty if you are under age 59 1/2. Make sure you talk to your financial adviser to determine the option that is right for you.

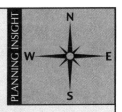

Record the information regarding your
company-sponsored retirement plans in the space provided.

Employer name	Account number	Owner	Current value

employee benefits contact		type of plan	☐ 401(k) ☐ 457 Plan
			☐ 403(b) ☐ Simple IRA

taxpayer I.D.	primary beneficiary	contingent beneficiary

notes and locations of records

Employer name	Account number	Owner	Current value

employee benefits contact		type of plan	☐ 401(k) ☐ 457 Plan
			☐ 403(b) ☐ Simple IRA

taxpayer I.D.	primary beneficiary	contingent beneficiary

notes and locations of records

Employer name	Account number	Owner		Current value

employee benefits contact			type of plan	☐ 401(k) ☐ 457 Plan
				☐ 403(b) ☐ Simple IRA

taxpayer I.D.	primary beneficiary	contingent beneficiary

notes and locations of records

Employer name	Account number	Owner		Current value

employee benefits contact			type of plan	☐ 401(k) ☐ 457 Plan
				☐ 403(b) ☐ Simple IRA

taxpayer I.D.	primary beneficiary	contingent beneficiary

notes and locations of records

Total value of my employer-sponsored plans	$

Pensions

While defined benefit pension plans are becoming less common, there are still millions of Americans that work for companies offering such plans. Simply stated, a pension is a sum of money paid regularly by a company as a retirement benefit as consideration for an employee's years of service to the company. With a 401(k), the employee is largely responsible for contributions to the plan; it is therefore called a defined *contribution* plan. By contrast, the employer is largely responsible for contributions to a pension plan; the pension is therefore often referred to as a defined *benefit* plan.

Record the information regarding your pensions in the space provided.

Employer name	Account number	Owner	Monthly benefit
employee benefits contact		death benefit	Lump sum: $ _____ Monthly: $_____
taxpayer I.D.	primary beneficiary	contingent beneficiary	
notes and locations of records			

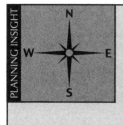

PLANNING INSIGHT

Pension plans vary considerably from company to company. If you purchased our Document Organizer with this book, place any new reports or memos regarding your employee benefit programs in the "Financial" section. In addition, if you receive an annual summary of your accumulated benefits, make sure you file it as well. Be sure to review those summaries closely, as it is best to straighten out any problems early on, rather than waiting until you retire and having your benefits delayed.

Employer name	Account number	Owner	Monthly benefit

| employee benefits contact | | death benefit | Lump sum: $ _____ |
| | | | Monthly: $_____ |

taxpayer I.D.	primary beneficiary	contingent beneficiary

notes and locations of records		

Employer name	Account number	Owner	Monthly benefit

| employee benefits contact | | death benefit | Lump sum: $ _____ |
| | | | Monthly: $_____ |

taxpayer I.D.	primary beneficiary	contingent beneficiary

notes and locations of records		

Employer name	Account number	Owner	Monthly benefit

| employee benefits contact | | death benefit | Lump sum: $ _____ |
| | | | Monthly: $_____ |

taxpayer I.D.	primary beneficiary	contingent beneficiary

notes and locations of records		

Total value of my pension plans	$

Annuities

Annuities are investment contracts between you and an insurance company that are designed for retirement. They allow you to invest tax-deferred, and you have the option to turn your assets into an income you cannot outlive. Annuities can be either fixed or variable. Fixed annuities pay a specific interest rate, while variable annuities can fluctuate based on the value of the stocks and bonds in which they are invested. As with 401(k)s and IRAs, taking money out of an annuity prior to age 59 1/2 can result in taxes and a 10% IRS penalty. Record the information regarding your annuities in the space provided.

Annuity company	Account number	Owner	Annuitant
account representative	type of annuity ☐ Variable ☐ Fixed		current value
taxpayer I.D.	primary beneficiary	contingent beneficiary	
notes and locations of records			

Annuity company	Account number	Owner	Annuitant
account representative	type of annuity ☐ Variable ☐ Fixed		current value
taxpayer I.D.	primary beneficiary	contingent beneficiary	
notes and locations of records			

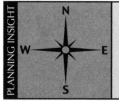

PLANNING INSIGHT

While there are certain benefits to investing in annuities (for example, tax-deferral, death benefit, lifetime income, etc.), it is important to understand the costs. Make sure to ask your financial adviser to explain the costs involved, as well as how he or she will be compensated.

Annuity company	Account number	Owner	Annuitant

account representative	type of annuity	☐ Variable ☐ Fixed	current value

taxpayer I.D.	primary beneficiary	contingent beneficiary

notes and locations of records

Annuity company	Account number	Owner	Annuitant

account representative	type of annuity	☐ Variable ☐ Fixed	current value

taxpayer I.D.	primary beneficiary	contingent beneficiary

notes and locations of records

Total value of my annuities	$

Education Savings Accounts

Paying for college is expensive. In fact, a child born today can expect to spend close to $200,000 for four years of college at a public school. Because of this, more and more parents are beginning to set aside money to help their children pay for their education. Thankfully, there are many tools available to help make saving for college easier than ever. We will discuss below the three main ways to save for college, and then there is space for you to record the details related to your education savings accounts. As we have said before, Congress often makes changes to the laws governing savings, and you should always speak with your financial adviser to obtain the most current information available.

529 Plans

529 Plans are the newest type of college savings vehicle. They are popular because the parent (or owner) retains control of the account even after the child (or beneficiary) reaches the age of majority. They are also popular because there are high contribution limits; earnings can grow free from Federal tax; and withdrawals for qualified higher education expenses are free from Federal tax.

Coverdell Education Savings Accounts

This type of account has similar tax treatment as the 529 Plan but differs in other areas. For example, you may contribute only if your income is below a certain level, and contribution limits are much lower than those in the 529 Plan. In addition, the beneficiary can assume control of the account when he/she reaches the age of majority, which means he/she can decide how to spend it. Often the parents that choose this type of account do so because they can use it to pay not only for college expenses, but also for expenses for kindergarten through high school.

Uniform Gift/Transfer to Minors Act Account (UGMA/UTMA)

Uniform Gift (or Transfer) to Minors Act accounts are the oldest of the three types of college savings vehicles. There are no income or contribution limits, but there are only limited tax benefits. As with the Coverdell Education Savings Accounts, the beneficiary assumes control of the account at the age of majority. Money can be spent for any use that benefits the child.

Owner/custodian	Beneficiary	Account number	Current value

institution		account representative	
taxpayer I.D.		type of account	☐ 529 Plan ☐ UGMA/UTMA ☐ Coverdell ESA
notes and locations of records			

Owner/custodian	Beneficiary	Account number	Current value

institution		account representative	
taxpayer I.D.		type of account	☐ 529 Plan ☐ UGMA/UTMA ☐ Coverdell ESA
notes and locations of records			

Owner/custodian	Beneficiary	Account number	Current value

institution		account representative	
taxpayer I.D.		type of account	☐ 529 Plan ☐ UGMA/UTMA ☐ Coverdell ESA
notes and locations of records			

Total value of my education savings accounts $

Real Estate

Owning your own home has always been an imortant part of the American dream. In addition, many people purchase rental properties, a vacation home, or commercial property for investment purposes. Real estate can be one of the most difficult assets to handle when a loved one dies, so it is important that you leave your heirs clear instructions. If you have any loans or mortgages on the real estate listed below, you can record them in the liability section on page 47. In the space below, record the information regarding your real estate holdings.

Address/legal description	Owner(s)	Estimated value

type of property	☐ Personal residence ☐ Investment property
	☐ Vacation property

date of purchase	purchase price	real estate taxes	tax valuation

notes and location of deed, mortgage information, and other records

Address/legal description	Owner(s)	Estimated value

type of property	☐ Personal residence ☐ Investment property
	☐ Vacation property

date of purchase	purchase price	real estate taxes	tax valuation

notes and location of deed, mortgage information, and other records

Address/legal description	Owner(s)	Estimated value

type of property	☐ Personal residence ☐ Vacation property	☐ Investment property	

date of purchase	purchase price	real estate taxes	tax valuation

notes and location of deed, mortgage information, and other records

Address/legal description	Owner(s)	Estimated value

type of property	☐ Personal residence ☐ Vacation property	☐ Investment property	

date of purchase	purchase price	real estate taxes	tax valuation

notes and location of deed, mortgage information, and other records

Total value of my real estate	$

Closely-Held Business

If you own your own business, it is probably one of your most valuable assets. If your business succeeds, it will quickly take on a financial life of its own. To plan for the management of the business and prepare a strategy for its continuation if you were to retire, sell the business, or pass away, it is vital that you keep your business records up to date. Record below the information regarding your business.

Name of business	Owner(s)	Percentage/shares	Estimated value

office address	type of business	☐ Sole proprietorship ☐ General partnership	☐ Limited partnership ☐ Limited liability co.	☐ S corporation ☐ C corporation

tax I.D. number	state I.D. number	nature of business

notes and business records

Name of business	Owner(s)	Percentage/shares	Estimated value

office address	type of business	☐ Sole proprietorship ☐ General partnership	☐ Limited partnership ☐ Limited liability co.	☐ S corporation ☐ C corporation

tax I.D. number	state I.D. number	nature of business

notes and business records

Total value of my closely-held businesses $

Automobiles and Other Vehicles

Anyone who has made a trip to the DMV at 4:00 p.m. on the last day of the month knows that dealing with your car can sometimes be a hassle. By recording below the information on your vehicles, you can ensure that your heirs have the information necessary to deal with this property should something happen to you. If you have a loan on any of these vehicles, you can record it in the liabilities section on page 48.

Vehicle description	Owner(s)	VIN number	Estimated value
Make: Model:			
notes and location of title, registration and other records			

Vehicle description	Owner(s)	VIN number	Estimated value
Make: Model:			
notes and location of title, registration and other records			

Vehicle description	Owner(s)	VIN number	Estimated value
Make: Model:			
notes and location of title, registration and other records			

AUTOMOBILES AND OTHER VEHICLES

Vehicle description	Owner(s)	VIN number	Estimated value
Make: Model:			
notes and location of title, registration and other records			

Vehicle description	Owner(s)	VIN number	Estimated value
Make: Model:			
notes and location of title, registration and other records			

Vehicle description	Owner(s)	VIN number	Estimated value
Make: Model:			
notes and location of title, registration and other records			

Total value of my vehicles	$

Tangible Personal Property

Over the years, you have likely accumulated jewelry, antiques, collectibles, and other valuable personal property. It is a good idea to have an inventory of those assets. Record below information regarding your tangible personal property.

Description of property	Owner(s)	Has the property been appraised?	Appraised/estimated value

notes and location of property, appraisal and other records

Description of property	Owner(s)	Has the property been appraised?	Appraised/estimated value

notes and location of property, appraisal and other records

Make sure to talk with your insurance agent about these items. Often your homeowner's policy does not cover jewelry, antiques or other collectibles. You may need to have a rider added to your policy to make sure that you are properly insured. Make sure that your insurance policy covers increases as you accumulate additional items or your current items appreciate. Again, if you purchased our Document Organizer with this workbook, include copies of any appraisals in the "Financial" section.

PLANNING INSIGHT

Description of property	Owner(s)	Has the property been appraised?	Appraised/estimated value

notes and location of property, appraisal and other records

Description of property	Owner(s)	Has the property been appraised?	Appraised/estimated value

notes and location of property, appraisal and other records

Description of property	Owner(s)	Has the property been appraised?	Appraised/estimated value

notes and location of property, appraisal and other records

Description of property	Owner(s)	Has the property been appraised?	Appraised/estimated value

notes and location of property, appraisal and other records

Total value of my tangible personal property	$

Miscellaneous Assets

This section is for recording assets, such as receivables, that don't quite fit in any of the other sections.
In the space provided below, record information regarding money that others owe you.

Money owed to you	Original amount	Original date	Interest rate

description		current balance	

date of first payment	payment amount	term

notes

Money owed to you	Original amount	Original date	Interest rate

description		current balance	

date of first payment	payment amount	term

notes

Total value of all receivables	$

Summary of Assets

There is space provided below for you to add up the value of your assets.
The page number of each asset class is provided to assist you.

Total Assets		
Bank accounts	Total on page 23	$
Brokerage accounts	Total on page 25	$
Individual retirement accounts	Total on page 28	$
Employer-sponsored plans	Total on page 31	$
Pensions	Total on page 33	$
Annuities	Total on page 35	$
Education savings accounts	Total on page 37	$
Cash value of life insurance	Total on page 58	$
Real estate	Total on page 39	$
Closely-held business	Total on page 40	$
Automobiles and other vehicles	Total on page 42	$
Tangible personal property	Total on page 44	$
Miscellaneous assets	Total on page 45	$
Total value of assets		$

Mortgage Information

On page 38 you recorded information relating to your real estate holdings.
If you have mortgages on any of those holdings, you may record that information here.

Losing a spouse can often mean losing all or part of your household income. This could force a surviving spouse to sell the family home because he/she is no longer able to make the payments. This situation can be avoided by planning ahead. Make sure there is enough insurance to cover the remaining balance on your mortgage in the event that the primary wage earner dies.

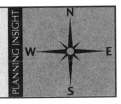

Property description	Owner(s)	Estimated value

lender name	contact information

original loan date	original loan amount	outstanding balance	interest rate

monthly payment amount	term of loan

notes and location of loan documents and payment book

Property description	Owner(s)	Estimated value

lender name	contact information

original loan date	original loan amount	outstanding balance	interest rate

monthly payment amount	term of loan

notes and location of loan documents and payment book

Total mortgage loan balance	$

Vehicle Debt

On page 41 you recorded information relating to your automobiles and other vehicles. If you have loans on any of those vehicles, you may record that information here.

Vehicle description	Owner(s)	Estimated value

lender name		contact information	

original loan date	original loan amount	monthly payment amount	current balance

term of loan		interest rate	

notes and location of loan documents and payment book

Vehicle description	Owner(s)	Estimated value

lender name		contact information	

original loan date	original loan amount	monthly payment amount	current balance

term of loan		interest rate	

notes and location of loan documents and payment book

Vehicle description	Owner(s)	Estimated value

lender name		contact information	

original loan date	original loan amount	monthly payment amount	current balance

term of loan		interest rate	

notes and location of loan documents and payment book

Total vehicle loan balance	$

Credit Card Information

In this section, record the details of all credit cards that you hold. In addition, if you carry a balance on any of those cards, record that information here.

Credit card name and number			Name(s) on card
issuing bank		customer service phone number	
outstanding balance	monthly payment	interest rate	scheduled pay-off date

Credit card name and number			Name(s) on card
issuing bank		customer service phone number	
outstanding balance	monthly payment	interest rate	scheduled pay-off date

Credit card name and number			Name(s) on card
issuing bank		customer service phone number	
outstanding balance	monthly payment	interest rate	scheduled pay-off date

CREDIT CARD INFORMATION

Credit card name and number		Name(s) on card

issuing bank	customer service phone number

outstanding balance	monthly payment	interest rate	scheduled pay-off date

Credit card name and number		Name(s) on card

issuing bank	customer service phone number

outstanding balance	monthly payment	interest rate	scheduled pay-off date

Credit card name and number		Name(s) on card

issuing bank	customer service phone number

outstanding balance	monthly payment	interest rate	scheduled pay-off date

Total credit card debt	$

Student Loans

As education costs have risen, student loans have become more prevalent. In fact, it is not unusual for students in law or medical school to graduate with tens of thousands, and sometimes hundreds of thousands of dollars, in school-related debt. If you have any student loans outstanding, record that information here.

Lender name		Lender contact information	
original loan amount		original loan date	
outstanding balance	monthly payment	interest rate	term of loan
location of loan documents and payment book			

Lender name		Lender contact information	
original loan amount		original loan date	
outstanding balance	monthly payment	interest rate	term of loan
location of loan documents and payment book			

Lender name		Lender contact information	
original loan amount		original loan date	
outstanding balance	monthly payment	interest rate	term of loan
location of loan documents and payment book			

Total student loan balance	$

Personal Loans/Lines of Credit

If you have drawn on a line of credit with your bank or other financial institution, record that information here. You may also use this space to record information on any personal or other miscellaneous loans you may have.

Lender name		Lender contact information	
original loan amount		original loan date	
outstanding balance	monthly payment	interest rate	term of loan
location of loan documents and payment book			

Lender name		Lender contact information	
original loan amount		original loan date	
outstanding balance	monthly payment	interest rate	term of loan
location of loan documents and payment book			

Lender name		Lender contact information	
original loan amount		original loan date	
outstanding balance	monthly payment	interest rate	term of loan
location of loan documents and payment book			

Total personal loans/lines of credit	$

Business Loans/Lines of Credit

If you have any business loans or have drawn on a business line of credit, record that information here.

Lender name		Lender contact information	

original loan amount		original loan date	

outstanding balance	monthly payment	interest rate	term of loan

location of loan documents and payment book

Lender name		Lender contact information	

original loan amount		original loan date	

outstanding balance	monthly payment	interest rate	term of loan

location of loan documents and payment book

Lender name		Lender contact information	

original loan amount		original loan date	

outstanding balance	monthly payment	interest rate	term of loan

location of loan documents and payment book

Total business loans/lines of credit	$

Summary of Liabilities

There is space below for you to add up the value of your liabilities.
The page number of each liability is provided to assist you.

Total liabilities		
Mortgage debt	Total on page 47	$
Vehicle debt	Total on page 48	$
Credit card debt	Total on page 50	$
Student loans	Total on page 51	$
Personal loans/lines of credit	Total on page 52	$
Business loans/lines of credit	Total on page 53	$
Total value of liabilities		$

By subtracting your total liabilites from the total value of your assets listed
on page 46, you can determine your net worth.

Net worth		
Assets	Total on page 46	$
Liabilities	Total on page 54	$
Net worth		$

www.ifsomethinghappenstome.com

Section 3
Insurance

Insurance is essential to every person's financial well-being. Determining what types are appropriate and how much coverage you need, however, can be a complex and often confusing process. In this section we will talk about whether and when certain types of insurance are appropriate. We will also give you some accepted rules of thumb for determining how much of a specific type of insurance you might need. There is also space for you to record details about your different policies.

In this section:

- ☐ Life Insurance
- ☐ Health Insurance
- ☐ Disability Insurance
- ☐ Long-Term Care Insurance
- ☐ Homeowner's Insurance
- ☐ Home Contents
- ☐ Auto Insurance
- ☐ Dental Insurance
- ☐ Umbrella Insurance
- ☐ Renter's Insurance

"In 1995, my husband died in an accident on the way home from a business trip. It was a devastating loss for my children and me. Thankfully, we had enough life insurance to take care of the family. I eventually went back to work, but the insurance helped to supplement my income and to fund our children's college education."

Amanda B.

Insurance is very complex. It is a contract between you and the insurance company. You should always work with an insurance professional to determine the types and amounts of coverage appropriate for you.

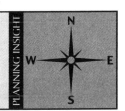

PLANNING INSIGHT

Life Insurance

Do you need life insurance? The main purpose of life insurance is to replace a person's income in the event of his/her death. Generally speaking, if you have people relying on your income, you need life insurance. It can also be a useful tool in other circumstances, such as estate planning or business succession planning.

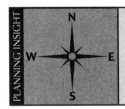

If both spouses work, and the amount of money you have to buy insurance is limited, cover the primary wage earner first. If one spouse does not work outside the home, you should purchase enough insurance on him or her to cover things like childcare, housekeeping and any other services that you would need to hire someone else to perform.

Once you decide whether you need life insurance, you will need to determine how much you need. While you don't want to over-insure, you do want to make sure that you purchase enough to replace the insured's income, pay for burial expenses, and pay off any debts you have incurred. Many advisers recommend purchasing insurance worth approximately five times your annual income. Since every family is unique, however, we have included a worksheet below that will help you determine your need.

Step 1   Determine what annual income the surviving spouse and dependents will need.

A: $ _____

Step 2   If the surviving spouse will have income sources in addition to the insurance, add those up and subtract them from the number you came up with in Step one. For example, a surviving spouse might have income from his or her own job, earnings on investments, or income from Social Security.

B: $ _____

C: $ _____ (A minus B)

Step 3   In order to replace a person's income indefinitely, you would need to invest the proceeds from the insurance settlement and live off the interest without touching the principal. Therefore, if you thought your after-tax returns would average 6%, you would divide the number you came up with on line C above by .06. If you think you would be more aggressive with your investments, you could divide by a larger percent or vice versa if you would be more conservative.

D: C/ .06 = $ _____

Step 4

There are a few adjustments we need to make to line D in order to arrive at a final number. First of all, your family will have certain expenses at the time of a death that are not factored into your typical annual salary needs. There is no way to know for certain what these expenses will be, but you can ask your attorney and your financial adviser to help you make an estimate.

E:
Funeral expenses	$	_____
Medical costs	$	_____
Estate taxes	$	_____
Trustee or probate fees	$	_____
Debts to be paid	$	_____
Emergency expenses	$	_____
Children's education	$	_____
Other	$	_____
Total	$	_____

Step 5

Add the total from Step 3 to the total from Step 4.

F: $ _____ + $ _____ (Step 3 plus Step 4) = $ _____

Step 6

Finally, subtract any assets that survivors could use to meet their needs from the number that you came up with on line F. As an example, they could access money in your retirement plans, or there may be proceeds from other insurance policies.

G:
Other life insurance	$	_____
Cash and other savings	$	_____
IRA or 401(k)	$	_____
Other	$	_____
Total	$	_____

Total of F minus G = Total face value of life insurance that you may need.

$ _____ - $ _____ = $ _____

Once you have determined how much insurance you may need, you should meet with your insurance agent to review your calculations and determine what type of life insurance would best meet your needs. Once you have done this, make sure to record the details of your policy in the space provided on page 58.

Policy owner	Insurance company			Policy type/number

insurance agent		telephone number	face amount	cash value

beneficiary	notes and location of documents

Policy owner	Insurance company			Policy type/number

insurance agent		telephone number	face amount	cash value

beneficiary	notes and location of documents

Policy owner	Insurance company			Policy type/number

insurance agent		telephone number	face amount	cash value

beneficiary	notes and location of documents

Policy owner	Insurance company			Policy type/number

insurance agent		telephone number	face amount	cash value

beneficiary	notes and location of documents

Total face amount of coverage	$
Total cash value of coverage	$

Health Insurance

Most people obtain their health insurance coverage from their employer. The cost of care, and consequently the cost of premiums, has been rising so rapidly, however, that many employers are making significant changes to their policies, as well as passing on some of the costs to their employees. As employees take on this more active role, it is important that they understand the details of their health coverage. This section will assist you toward that end.

Group vs. Individual Plans

As we mentioned earlier, most people get their coverage as part of a group through their employer. If a group plan is not available, then you will need to purchase an individual plan. Group plans are typically preferred because they are generally more comprehensive and have lower rates. You are also automatically accepted into the group plan if you are part of the group. With an individual policy, you will need to get a physical examination and go through the medical underwriting process. As a result, your premiums will be based, in part, on your age and health.

Types of Health Insurance

There are many different types of health insurance plans available today. Some, like catastrophic coverage, pay for only specific services, while others, like preferred provider organizations (PPOs) pay for a broad range of services. Make sure to understand what type of policy you have and how it works. Encourage your employer to have educational meetings for the employees. The emergency room is not a good place to learn about what your policy covers.

Record the information regarding your health policies in the space provided.

Health coverage provided by my employer

Employer	
Company address	
Company telephone	
Employee benefits contact at my company	
Health insurance provider	
Address	
Telephone number	
Plan name	
Plan type	
Member or policy number	
Person(s) covered by this policy	
A summary of my policy is located:	

Health coverage provided by my employer

Employer	
Company address	
Company telephone	
Employee benefits contact at my company	
Health insurance provider	
Address	
Telephone number	
Plan name	
Plan type	
Member or policy number	
Person(s) covered by this policy	
A summary of my policy is located:	

Individual health policy

Insurance company	
Address	
Telephone	
Customer service contact information	
Insurance agent name	
Insurance agent telephone number	
Plan name	
Plan type	
Member or policy number	
Person(s) covered by this policy	
A summary of my policy is located:	

Individual health policy

Insurance company	
Address	
Telephone	
Customer service contact information	
Insurance agent name	
Insurance agent telephone number	
Plan name	
Plan type	
Member or policy number	
Person(s) covered by this policy	
A summary of my policy is located:	

Disability Insurance

Between the ages of 35 and 65, we are 3 times more likely to become disabled than to die; yet only 40% of people in this age group have disability insurance vs. 70% who have life insurance. For most people, being unable to work due to a disability would have a significant negative impact on their financial well-being. You can manage this risk by purchasing disability insurance.

How Disability Insurance Works

If you are the beneficiary of a disability policy, and you become disabled (by the insurance company's definition), you become eligible for benefits under the policy. Typically, insurance companies define disability as an inability to perform the duties of your particular occupation. A less advantageous policy may require you to be unable to perform any occupation for which you are suited, based on your education, training, and experience.

When you meet the insurance company's definition of disability, the policy will generally replace a certain percentage of your income while you remain disabled.

What To Look For In A Disability Policy

As with all types of insurance coverage, disability insurance can vary greatly from policy to policy. Make sure to discuss the following items with your insurance agent:

- Income benefits
- Elimination period
- Definition of disability
- Waiver of premiums
- Cost of living adjustment

Policy information

Person(s) covered by this policy	
My policy is: (circle one)	Individual Through work
Insurance company	
Customer service contact information	
Insurance agent name	
Insurance agent telephone number	
Member or policy number	
A summary of my policy is located:	

Policy information

Person(s) covered by this policy	
My policy is: (circle one)	Individual Through work
Insurance company	
Customer service contact information	
Insurance agent name	
Insurance agent telephone number	
Member or policy number	
A summary of my policy is located:	

Long-Term Care Insurance

As we have helped people plan for their long-term care needs over the years, we have often said that you are an adult once, but you are a child twice. As we age, our minds and bodies begin to fail, and we often need to rely on others for care.

Only a small percent of deaths in America happen totally unexpectedly. The rest of us see the end approaching. Often the planning we have done ahead of time will determine our quality of life during these final years. In a study on dying in America, the president of the National Association of Attorneys General said, "Seventy percent of Americans want to die at home, free from pain, surrounded by family and friends; seventy percent will die in an institution, in pain, without family and friends."

This need not be the case. As the population ages, long-term care insurance is becoming more and more prevalent. People want to make sure that if they get to a point where they need assistance with the activities of daily living (ADLs for short), they are able to receive quality care either at home or in a facility of their choice for a price that does not wipe them out financially. A desire not to be a burden on other family members is also an often-quoted reason for obtaining long-term care insurance. This section will discuss how long-term care works and what to look for in a policy.

How Long-Term Care Insurance Works

As with most insurance contracts, there are myriad long-term care policies. In general, however, a long-term care policy pays a specific dollar amount for each day of care that is covered by the policy. These covered services can include home health care, respite care, adult day care, care in an assisted living facility, or nursing home care. The policy is usually triggered when you need help performing the normal activities of daily living, such as bathing, eating, dressing, toileting, continence, and transfer.

Medicare provides only very limited nursing home coverage. Medicaid will pay most nursing home costs, but you need to qualify by being both sick and poor. Consequently, it is not desirable to be in a position in which you are relying on the government to meet your long-term care needs. Work with your advisers to ensure that you have a plan in place.

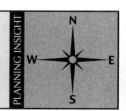

Do You Need Long-Term Care Insurance?

Long-term care costs can be very expensive, and they vary based on the type of care you need and where you get it. Currently, the average cost of one year in a nursing home is approximately $66,000. That's about $181 per day. Clearly, the costs are significant enough to consider insuring against. Some of the most common reasons given for purchasing a policy are:

- To preserve assets for heirs
- To have peace of mind
- To avoid being a burden to friends or family
- To be able to get into your choice of facilities
- To be cared for at home as long as possible
- To avoid relying on the government (Medicaid)

You should probably not buy long-term care insurance if:

- You don't have significant assets to protect
- You can't afford the premiums
- Your only source of income is Social Security

What To Look For When Buying a Policy:

☐ A Strong Insurer – You want to make sure that your insurance company outlives you. You should generally buy only from a company that is rated A or better by a reputable rating agency. Ask your agent to provide you with the financial rating of the companies he or she is recommending.

☐ Inflation Protection – Since medical costs are rising rapidly, you want your coverage limits to rise with it. You may be able to purchase one day in a nursing home in your area now for about $150, but that same day might cost you $350 ten years from now. It is generally good to get a policy that compounds 5% annually.

☐ Broad Choices – You want your policy to cover not only nursing home care, but also home care and assisted living care.

☐ Policy Language – Typically, insurance contracts are not written in your favor. Some companies have more customer-friendly policies than others, however. Ask your agent to explain the fine print to you.

If you have obtained a long-term care insurance policy, record the details below.

Long-term care policy details

1. Insurance company information

   Name of company _____

   Address _____

   Phone number _____ E-Mail _____

2. Agent information

   Agent's name _____

   Address _____

   Phone number _____ E-Mail _____

3. Policy information

   Date purchased _____

   Policy number _____

   Annual premium _____

   Who does this policy cover? _____

4. Type of long-term care policy

   _____ Comprehensive (nursing home, assisted living, home and community care)

   _____ Nursing home only

   _____ Home care only

   _____ Other

5. Length of time policy benefits cover

   _____ Limited (write in the number of years here _____)

   _____ Unlimited

6 How long is the waiting period before benefits begin? _____

7. How often do I pay premiums: _____ Annually _____ Semi-annually _____ Other

   Amount of premiums: _____ Annually _____ Semi-annually _____ Other

8. The person to be notified if I forget to pay the premium: _____

   Address _____ Phone number _____

9. I keep this long-term care policy in the following location:

   _____

Homeowner's Insurance

If you have a house, you should have homeowner's insurance. In fact, if you have a mortgage on the property, your lender will likely require it. Homeowner policies typically come in two sections: Section I covers your property, and Section II provides personal liability coverage.

What to Consider When Buying a Policy

When buying homeowner's insurance, your main concern is to get the appropriate amount of coverage at a price you can afford. At a minimum, your policy should cover the replacement cost of your home and its contents, as well as personal liability for incidents that happen on your property. You may also want to obtain flood insurance or earthquake insurance if you live in areas susceptible to these risks.

Some Ideas to Control the Cost of Your Homeowner's Insurance

1 Raise your deductible

It is often not practical to have a low deductible on your house. Since insurance companies have become more strict about the number of claims they allow before discontinuing your coverage, it is usually better to pay for smaller losses yourself and file claims only if you have a large loss. The higher deductible will lower your premiums.

2 Safety devices

Installing safety devices such as burglar alarms, fire suppression systems, and dead bolts can help lower your premiums.

3 Choice of neighborhood

If you live in a high-crime area, your premiums will likely be higher.

It is generally a good idea to have a higher deductible on your homeowner's policy and take care of small claims yourself. This will help reduce the cost of your policy. If you have frequent claims on your policy, you run the risk of having your coverage dropped by your insurer. Since your mortgage lender will require you to have coverage, you will likely have to pay much higher rates at a company that insures higher risk individuals.

Homeowner's policy details

Insurance company	
Customer service number	
My insurance agent	
Agent's phone number	
Home covered (primary, vacation, etc.)	
Policy number	
A summary of this policy is located:	

Homeowner's policy details

Insurance company	
Customer service number	
My insurance agent	
Agent's phone number	
Home covered (primary, vacation, etc.)	
Policy number	
A summary of this policy is located:	

Homeowner's policy details

Insurance company	
Customer service number	
My insurance agent	
Agent's phone number	
Home covered (primary, vacation, etc.)	
Policy number	
A summary of this policy is located:	

Home Contents

If your house burns down, you may have a difficult time remembering (or proving you owned) all of the items you lost in the fire; therefore, it is often a good idea to inventory the contents of your home. You can either do this by walking around the house with a camcorder and giving a guided tour of your personal belongings, or by making a room-by-room list of your home's contents. Regardless of which method you use, make sure to store the inventory somewhere other than your home. If you choose to make a written inventory, we have provided a worksheet below.

Home Inventory Worksheet

Living room

Article	Quantity	Date purchased	Original cost

Dining room

Article	Quantity	Date purchased	Original cost

Bedrooms

Article	Quantity	Date purchased	Original cost

Bathrooms

Article	Quantity	Date purchased	Original cost

Laundry

Article	Quantity	Date purchased	Original cost

Kitchen

Article	Quantity	Date purchased	Original cost

Home Office

Article	Quantity	Date purchased	Original cost

Garage / Lawn / Patio

Article	Quantity	Date purchased	Original cost

Basement / Attic / Storage

Article	Quantity	Date purchased	Original cost

Auto Insurance

It is a good idea to review your auto insurance coverage annually. Your auto insurance is typically made up of seven different areas of coverage, each having its own premium. Those include:

1) Bodily injury liability
   This covers you if you injure or kill someone while operating your vehicle.

2) Personal injury
   This will usually cover the medical expenses of the injured driver or passengers in your car.

3) Universal motorist coverage
   This provides coverage if you are injured in an accident caused by an uninsured driver.

4) Comprehensive physical damage
   This covers losses resulting from something other than a collision (for example, theft, flood, fire).

5) Collision
   This provides coverage if your vehicle is damaged as a result of hitting or being hit by another vehicle or object.

6) Property damage liability
   This provides coverage for property damage as a result of an accident.

7) Rental car reimbursement
   This covers the cost of renting a car while your car is being repaired because of a covered accident.

Some tips to control the cost of your auto insurance

1) Obey the laws
   Most companies offer a safe driver discount based on whether you've had any tickets in the last 3 years.

2) Drive less
   A short commute or the use of public transportation will usually lower your premiums.

3) Type of vehicle
   Driving newer, more expensive, sporty cars will usually result in higher premiums.

4) Safety devices
   Airbags, anti-lock brakes, and anti-theft devices should all help to lower your premiums.

5) Higher deductibles
   Raising your deductibles or dropping certain elements of your coverage
   (for example, collision if you have an old vehicle) will help you reduce your rates.

Auto insurance

Vehicle covered	
Insurance company	
Customer service number	
My insurance agent	
Agent's phone number	
Policy number	
A summary of this policy is located:	

Auto insurance

Vehicle covered	
Insurance company	
Customer service number	
My insurance agent	
Agent's phone number	
Policy number	
A summary of this policy is located:	

Auto insurance

Vehicle covered	
Insurance company	
Customer service number	
My insurance agent	
Agent's phone number	
Policy number	
A summary of this policy is located:	

Auto insurance

Vehicle covered	
Insurance company	
Customer service number	
My insurance agent	
Agent's phone number	
Policy number	
A summary of this policy is located:	

Dental Insurance

Dental coverage comes in many different forms and is often offered as an employee benefit by employers. Premiums are paid to the insurance company, and the company covers a percentage of certain dental expenses.

Typical Features of Dental Plans

- Long probationary period on certain services

- High deductibles

- Annual dollar limit on benefits

- Freedom to choose your own dentist

Below is a chart of dental services and procedures, the usual coverage for those services, and the common waiting period before accessing those services.

Dental procedures and services		
Procedure or service	Usually covered?	Waiting period?
Diagnostic or preventive	Yes	No
Restorative care (fillings)	Yes	Yes
Oral surgery (removal of wisdom teeth)	Yes	Yes
Endodontics (root canal)	Yes	Yes
Periodontics (gum disease)	Yes	Yes
Prosthodontics (dentures)	Yes, at reduced rate	Yes
Orthodontics (braces)	Yes, at reduced rate	Yes
Cosmetic services	No, unless related to an accident	N/A
Pre-existing conditions	No	N/A

Dental insurance policy

Name of insured	
My policy is: (circle one)	An individual policy Through work
Dental insurance company	
Customer service contact	
My dentist (or other dental professional)	
My dentist's phone number	
My policy number	
My dental policy is located:	

Dental insurance policy

Name of insured	
My policy is: (circle one)	An individual policy Through work
Dental insurance company	
Customer service contact	
My dentist (or other dental professional)	
My dentist's phone number	
My policy number	
My dental policy is located:	

Umbrella Insurance

Both your home and auto policy provide (limited) coverage for personal liability. It can sometimes be a good idea to buy a supplementary policy to increase this amount of coverage. These policies are typically called umbrella policies; they are relatively affordable and can be easily coordinated with your existing insurance policies.

Umbrella policies are designed to kick in when your other policies have reached their maximum payout amounts. For example, let's assume someone slipped and fell on your driveway and sued you for $1 million. If he won, your homeowner's policy would pay the maximum amount allowed in the policy (usually about $300,000). If you didn't have any further coverage, you would be responsible for the remaining $700,000. If you had a $1 million umbrella policy, however, the policy would cover that remaining $700,000.

Are you a good candidate for an umbrella policy?

- ☐ Do you travel often?
- ☐ Do you entertain frequently?
- ☐ Do you operate a home-based business with employees or clients coming to your house regularly?
- ☐ Do you have teenage drivers in the house? (Teenagers are typically more likely to be involved in auto accidents.)

My umbrella policy details				
Insurance company				
Customer service number				
My insurance agent				
Agent's phone number				
Supplements (circle all that apply)	Home	Autos	Boat	Other
Policy number(s)				
A summary of this policy is located:				

Renter's Insurance

If you are a renter, your landlord's insurance does not cover your personal property. If your apartment burned down, the structure would be covered, but without renter's insurance, items such as your clothes, furniture, television, computer, stereo, jewelry, and bicycle would not be covered. Renter's insurance will typically cover the contents of your home or apartment against loss from fire or smoke, vandalism, theft, windstorm, explosion, and water damage from plumbing. It will also provide a certain level of liability coverage for people injured on your premises and will pay certain legal defense costs if you are sued.

My renter's policy details	
Insurance company	
Customer service number	
My insurance agent	
Agent's phone number	
Policy number	
A summary of this policy is located:	

As with homeowner's insurance, it is a good idea to inventory your personal property in case you need to make a claim on your renter's policy.

Section 4
Estate Planning

On the following pages, we have described the legal documents that form the foundation for most estate plans and have provided you a place to record the specifics of your plan. This information should help you to evaluate the plan you have in place, identify the tools you need, and give your family the information they need to help carry out your plan.

In this section:

☐ Durable Power of Attorney for Finance
☐ Durable Power of Attorney for Health Care
☐ Wills
☐ Revocable Living Trusts
☐ Irrevocable Trusts

"Two years ago, my parents were involved in a horrible traffic accident. My dad was killed instantly, and my mother spent the next month in intensive care, unable to communicate with anyone. Making a horrible situation worse, they did not have a living will or any powers of attorney. Without clear instructions and authority from our parents, my siblings and I were forced to guess at their wishes."

Mitch J.

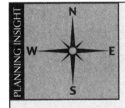

There are three objectives that you should keep in mind as you plan your estate:

1) Make sure that your plan passes your property to the correct people.

This is a simple goal, but one many people fail to achieve. By working with your advisers, you can put a plan in place that uses the right estate planning tools to ensure that your wishes regarding the handling of your property will be honored. If your plan fails to meet this goal, you may leave a legacy of financial hardship and conflict by allowing property to pass to people that you never intended to include in your estate.

2) Make sure that your plan designates the correct people to take charge.

If you do not plan correctly, power over your finances may fall into the hands of someone that you never intended. If you were to become disabled or die, your plan should allow the people you have selected to take over and be provided with the instructions and authority they need to keep your property in order.

3) Make sure that your plan minimizes expense, hassle, and taxes.

As good stewards, we should try to preserve the property that has been entrusted to us. If you do not plan properly, your property may be eroded through payment of unnecessary taxes and expenses. There is no reason to pay more tax or expense than you owe. We should all arrange our affairs so that we owe as little as possible.

Durable Power of Attorney for Finance

A Durable Power of Attorney is a simple and inexpensive legal document that authorizes a person you have chosen, known as your "Agent," to step in and manage your day-to-day financial decisions if you become incapacitated.

We all need a Durable Power of Attorney, regardless of how much or how little property we own, to provide for the ongoing management of our financial affairs if we cannot make decisions for ourselves. If you become incapacitated, and you have not signed a Durable Power of Attorney, your family may be required to ask a court to appoint a conservator to handle your property under the court's supervision.

Issues to Consider When Creating or Changing Your Durable Power of Attorney

1) Your agents

Your first decision involves choosing an agent to make decisions for you. You may designate your spouse, adult child, a family member, a close friend, or anyone else you might choose to serve. The person you choose should be a competent adult who can be trusted to handle your financial decisions carefully and who is willing to accept responsibility for handling your property. Your agent does not need to live in the same city you do, but in the event of a long-term disability, it is important that he or she be available to help for long periods of time. You should name at least one alternate agent to serve if your first choice is unavailable.

2) Effective date

Next, you need to determine when the power granted to your agent under the Durable Power of Attorney should come into effect. Typically, a Durable Power of Attorney is "presently effective," drafted to take effect on the date it is signed. If you are reluctant to grant someone broad powers to act on your behalf when you are capable of acting yourself, a "springing power" can be prepared that allows the Durable Power of Attorney to spring into effect upon the happening of a specific event, such as a doctor's certification that you are incapacitated. The difficulty with springing powers is that the document must set clear conditions under which the Durable Power of Attorney comes into effect, and your agent may be required to provide proof, such as a letter from your physician, that the conditions have been met in order to have authority to act.

> "As my mother has gotten older, I have taken an increasingly active role in helping her with her daily activities. She recently made the decision to move into an assisted living facility. By her giving me shared power of attorney, I was able to handle all of the paperwork involved in the sale of her house and speak with her financial adviser on her behalf. This freed her up to focus on her move and to adjust to her new surroundings."
>
> Roberta H.

3) Extent of authority

Lastly, you must decide how much and what type of power to give to your agent. The extent of power granted under the Durable Power of Attorney would normally be very broad, allowing your agent to do most things you could do for yourself, such as pay your bills, handle your accounts, manage investments, deal with your insurance, pay your taxes, collect Social Security or other government benefits, and many other important tasks. You may, however, limit the power granted to your agent to very specific actions.

Important Information to Record Related to Your Durable Power of Attorney

If you have Durable Powers of Attorney in place, record in the space below the information about these documents, so it is easily accessible to you and your family. If you have questions about your Durable Power of Attorney, don't hesitate to ask your estate planning attorney for assistance.

Principal (name of person signing)	Date of signing
agent	**alternate agent(s)**
presently effective or springing power?	☐ Presently effective ☐ Springing power Conditions:
notes and location of original document	

Principal (name of person signing)	Date of signing
agent	**alternate agent(s)**
presently effective or springing power?	☐ Presently effective ☐ Springing power Conditions:
notes and location of original document	

Durable Power of Attorney for Health Care

Great advancements in health care continue to extend the length and quality of our lives. This progress has one negative side effect: Many people fear that they might be kept alive for an indefinite period of time through the use of respirators, intravenous feeding and hydration, and other artificial means, when death would be imminent under natural circumstances. To control the use of these treatments and determine who will handle your medical decisions in the event you are unable to make decisions for yourself, you need a Durable Power of Attorney for Health Care. This legal document is designed to make your wishes clear when you can no longer speak for yourself.

If you become incapacitated, and you have not signed a Durable Power of Attorney for Health Care, your family may be required to ask a court to appoint a guardian to handle your health care decisions. This can be a complicated and expensive process in which you do not have control over the court's decisions.

Issues to Consider When Creating or Changing Your Durable Power of Attorney for Health Care

1) Your agents

Again, your first decision involves choosing an agent to make your health care decisions. You may designate your spouse, adult child, a family member, a close friend, or anyone else you might choose to serve as your agent. The person you choose should be a competent adult who understands your desires and beliefs related to your health care, and is willing to accept responsibility to make your decisions. Your agent does not need to live in the same city as you do, but in the event of a long-term disability, it is important that he or she is available to be with you for long periods of time. You should designate one or more alternate agents to serve if your first choice is not available.

> "At just 23 years old, my husband and I were shocked to learn that some pain I had been experiencing in my neck was actually a large tumor. As my treatment progressed, we had our attorney prepare a health care directive that would help to guide my husband's decision making if I became incapacitated."
>
> Jessica L.

2) Health care directive

Next, you must decide if you wish to include a health care directive. Health care directives may take many forms and are called by many names (such as a living will), but include written instructions to your agent communicating your wishes regarding the withholding or withdrawal of certain life support equipment or medical procedures. Generally, health care providers must follow a health care directive or take all reasonable steps to arrange for your transfer to a provider who will follow your instructions.

3) Organ donation

A Durable Power of Attorney for Health Care is one of several methods that may be used to express your wishes regarding organ donation.

Important Information to Record Related to
Your Durable Power of Attorney for Health Care

If you have Durable Powers of Attorney for Health Care in place, record the information about these documents below. If you have questions about your Durable Power of Attorney for Health Care, don't hesitate to ask your estate planning attorney for assistance.

Principal (name of person signing)	Date of signing

agent	alternate agent(s)

health care directive or living will included?	☐ Yes ☐ No	organ donation provision included?	☐ Yes ☐ No

notes and location of original document

Principal (name of person signing)	Date of signing

agent	alternate agent(s)

health care directive or living will included?	☐ Yes ☐ No	organ donation provision included?	☐ Yes ☐ No

notes and location of original document

Wills

Wills are probably the most well-known, but often misunderstood, estate planning tools. A will is simply a legal document, with formal signing requirements, which states a person's instructions for the division and distribution of property to heirs at death.

Most people need a will, regardless of the size of their estate, to control the passing of property at death and to name a guardian for minor children. If you die without a will, the laws of your state of residence, or the laws of the states in which you own real estate, may control who inherits your property. State intestacy laws generally distribute property according to a rigid formula based upon how closely a person is related to you. Failure to make a will can cause conflict and additional expense for your family, and could leave your property to people that you never intended.

A will also provides a good backup plan when using other methods to transfer property. You need a will even if your assets are owned in joint tenancy, a revocable living trust, or in a manner in which a beneficiary is designated (retirement plans and life insurance) to guard against intestacy for property titled in your own name or in the event your joint tenant or beneficiary dies before you do.

Issues to Consider When Creating or Changing Your Will

Your estate planning attorney can prepare a will for you based upon information in the previous sections and your decisions regarding the following issues:

1) Personal representative
First, you must designate a personal representative, the person appointed to carry out the instructions described in your will. Your spouse, adult children, a family member, a close friend, or adviser is usually chosen to serve as personal representative because they can usually be trusted to handle your assets carefully. If your estate is large or complicated, a bank or trust company should be considered. Your will should name at least one successor personal representative to serve if your primary personal representative is not available.

2) Guardian
If you have minor children, plan on having children, or have a disabled adult child, your will should name a guardian to take on the parenting role for your children. This can be a very tough decision, but your parents, siblings, other family members, or close friends are usually chosen to serve because of existing relationships to the children. Your will should also name a successor guardian to act if your primary guardian is not available to serve. If parents die without a will, a court will appoint a guardian for their children based upon what the court believes to be in the best interest of the children, given the information it has available and often depending upon who volunteers.

3) Heirs
Lastly, you must decide who should receive your property, how much they should receive, and when they should receive it. There are as many different plans for division and distribution of property as there are families. Each family is unique, but the will would usually include provisions for passing your property to your spouse (if you are married), then on to your children, other family members, or favorite charities on the death of the surviving spouse. If you have minor children or adult children that need help managing money, your will can arrange for continued management of the property for the benefit of the children until they reach an age at which you think they can handle their inheritance on their own.

Important Information to Record Related to Your Will

If you have a will or wills in place, record below the information about these documents, so it is easily accessible to you and your family. If you have questions about your will, don't hesitate to ask your estate planning attorney for assistance.

Testator (name of person signing will)	Date of signing
personal representative	successor personal representative
guardian	successor guardian
notes and location of original document	

Testator (name of person signing will)	Date of signing
personal representative	successor personal representative
guardian	successor guardian
notes and location of original document	

Revocable Living Trusts

A revocable living trust is an agreement, created during your lifetime, between you as "settlor," the person who creates the trust, and a "trustee," the person who manages the property transferred to the trust. The trust agreement includes your instructions for the management, division, and distribution of the trust property to your beneficiaries. In most cases, the creator of the trust serves as his or her own trustee while living and able. A revocable trust is one in which you have the right to revoke or amend the trust and take out all property placed in the trust.

Revocable living trusts are often used as a will substitute, to control the passing of your property at death and avoid the expense and delay of probate. Unlike property passing by a will, property titled to a revocable living trust avoids probate because the trust instructions provide the trustee with authority to handle the assets without a court's supervision. There is nothing for the court to supervise because you have arranged ahead of time for the trustee to follow your instructions. It is important to note, though, that the trustee has authority to handle only those assets that have been titled into the name of the trust, either during your life, or by the use of beneficiary designations or a will after death.

Issues to Consider When Creating or Changing Your Revocable Living Trust

Your estate planning attorney can prepare a revocable living trust for you based upon the information in prior sections and your decisions regarding the following issues:

1) Trustee and successor trustees

As we said above, the creator of the trust will often serve as the trustee of the trust while he or she is living, but the trust should also designate at least two successor trustees to serve if the primary trustee dies or is incapacitated. You may designate your spouse, a family member, a close friend, or a bank or trust company to serve as trustee. The person you choose should be a competent adult who can be trusted to handle the trust assets carefully and is willing to accept responsibility for the property. If your estate is large or complicated, a financial professional or trust company should be considered.

2) Beneficiaries

As with a will, you must decide what instructions to give your trustee regarding the division and distribution of the trust property. Your trust should identify your beneficiaries and describe how much property they should receive and when they should receive it. If you have minor children or adult children that need help managing money, your trust can provide ongoing management of the property for your beneficiaries until they reach the age at which you think they can handle their portion of the trust property on their own.

3) Property

To make effective use of your revocable trust in saving probate expenses, after you have signed the trust document, there is an additional task you must complete. Your estate planning attorney and other advisers should help you through the process of transferring the title of your property to your revocable living trust. The instructions in your trust apply only to property actually titled to your trust or those assets that pass into your trust on death. Since the primary benefit of creating a trust is the avoidance of probate, it is advisable to review the ownership of your property periodically to make sure that your property will pass according to your trust instructions, free of probate.

Important Information to Record Related to Your Revocable Living Trust

If you have a revocable living trust in place, record below the information related to this document. If you have questions about your trust or how to title an asset to your trust, consult your estate planning attorney.

Settlor(s) (names of those creating the trust)	Date of signing

trustee(s)	successor trustee(s)

name of trust	trust taxpayer I.D. number

notes and location of original document	

Settlor(s) (names of those creating the trust)	Date of signing

trustee(s)	successor trustee(s)

name of trust	trust taxpayer I.D. number

notes and location of original document	

Irrevocable Trusts

The irrevocable trust is an estate planning tool generally used by individuals or couples with large estates that may be subject to the Federal estate tax. Irrevocable trusts may be used to transfer property from one generation to the next while avoiding estate taxes. This tool can also provide a readily available source of liquid assets, outside of the individual or couple's taxable estate, to pay for estate expenses, to pay taxes generated by other assets, or to meet other estate obligations. Once put in place, irrevocable trusts cannot be amended or revoked.

Important Information to Record Related to Your Irrevocable Trust

Irrevocable trusts are complicated estate planning tools that deal with several of the same trustee, beneficiary, and property questions as the revocable trust discussed previously. Be sure to consult your estate planning attorney, so he or she can help you carefully consider the estate and tax issues related to the preparation of these trusts. If you have an irrevocable trust in place, record below the information related to this document.

Settlor(s) (names of those creating the trust)	Date of signing
trustee(s) / successor trustee(s)	
name of trust / trust taxpayer I.D. number	
notes and location of original document	

Settlor(s) (names of those creating the trust)	Date of signing
trustee(s) / successor trustee(s)	
name of trust / trust taxpayer I.D. number	
notes and location of original document	

Section 5
Government Benefits

The government provides certain benefits that you and your family may be entitled to. These include Social Security, Veteran's Benefits, Medicare, and Medicaid. In this section we will discuss these programs, indicate who is eligible for benefits, and explain how to claim them.

In this section:

☐ Social Security
☐ Veteran's Benefits
☐ Medicare/Medicaid

"My husband died unexpectedly of a heart attack as we approached retirement. As a widow, I was able to begin collecting Social Security benefits early. This helped to supplement my income and enabled me to continue living in the home we had shared for so many years."

Jennifer K.

To make sure that your Social Security payments are being recorded properly, you should review them annually. You can do this by either reviewing the Social Security statement sent to you or by contacting the Social Security Administration to request a personalized benefit estimate. You can also obtain this form at your local Social Security office or on the web at www.ssa.gov.

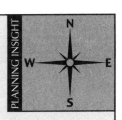

Social Security

Who Is Eligible For Benefits?

A person becomes eligible for Social Security benefits by paying into the system. In addition, when a person who has paid Social Security taxes dies, certain members of his or her family could be eligible for survivor benefits. According to the Social Security Administration, those eligible are:

- A widow/widower can receive reduced benefits as early as age 60 and full benefits at full retirement age.

- A disabled widow/widower can receive benefits as early as age 50.

- A widow/widower can receive benefits at any age if he or she is taking care of the deceased's child who is under age 16 or disabled, and receiving Social Security benefits.

- Unmarried children under age 18, or up to age 19 if they are attending high school full-time, are eligible for benefits. In certain circumstances, stepchildren, grandchildren, or adopted children may also be eligible for benefits.

- Children at any age who were disabled before age 22 and remain disabled are eligible for benefits.

- Dependent parents age 62 or older are eligible for benefits.

How To Contact The Social Security Administration

- Call them directly at 1-800-772-1213. If you are deaf or hard of hearing, you may call their "TTY" number, 1-800-325-0778.

- Call or visit your local Social Security office. You can find your local office in the phone book or by visiting www.ssa.gov.

- While the Social Security Administration does not have offices outside the United States, many of the American embassies and consulates have specially trained personnel that can handle questions and take applications for benefits.

Documents Needed To Apply For Survivor Benefits

- Proof of death from either the funeral home or a death certificate
- Your birth certificate
- Your marriage certificate if you're the widow or widower
- Proof of U.S. citizenship, or proof of lawful alien status if you were born outside the United States
- Your divorce papers if you're applying as a surviving divorced spouse
- Dependent children's Social Security numbers
- Deceased worker's most recent W-4 forms or Federal self-employment tax return

Public records like your birth certificate and marriage or divorce records must be the originals or copies certified by the issuing agency. The Social Security Administration will return these documents to you.

Helpful Hints

When you apply for survivor's benefits, there are certain questions the Social Security Administration will ask you. They suggest that you jot down answers to the following questions ahead of time in order to speed the process along:

- Your name and Social Security number

- Your birth name (if different)

- The deceased's name, gender, Social Security number, date of birth, date of death, and place of death

- Your date of birth and place of birth (state or foreign country)

- Whether a public or religious record of your birth was made before age 5

- The state or foreign country of the worker's fixed permanent residence at the time of death

- Whether you or anyone else has ever filed for Social Security benefits, Medicare, or Supplemental Security Income on your behalf

- Whether the deceased ever filed for Social Security benefits, Medicare, or Supplemental Security Income

- Whether you have been unable to work because of illnesses, injuries, or conditions at any time within the past 14 months

- Whether the deceased was unable to work because of illnesses, injuries, or conditions at any time during the 14 months before his or her death

- Whether you or the deceased worker were ever in the active military service before 1968 and, if so, the dates of service and whether you receive or are eligible to receive a pension from a military or Federal civilian agency

- Whether you or the deceased worked for the railroad industry

- Whether you or the deceased ever earned social security credits under another country's social security system

- Whether you qualified for or expect to receive a pension or annuity based on your own employment with the Federal government

- The names, dates of birth, and Social Security numbers of any of your or the deceased's former spouses

- The dates of each of your marriages and, for marriages that have ended, how and when they ended

- The dates of each of the deceased's marriages and how and when they ended

- The amount of the deceased's earnings in the year of death and the year prior to death

- Whether the deceased had earnings in all years since 1978

- The amount of your earnings for this year, last year and next year

- Whether the deceased had a parent who was dependent on the deceased for half of his or her support at the time of the deceased's death or at the time he or she became disabled

- Whether you were living with the deceased worker at the time of death

- The month you want your benefits to begin

- If you are within 3 months of age 65, whether you want to enroll in Supplemental Medical Insurance (Part B of Medicare)

- The name of your bank and your account number, so your benefits can be directly deposited into your account

Veteran's Benefits

If you served in the military, you and members of your family may be entitled to certain benefits. These benefits cover areas such as health, education, compensation and pension, life insurance, vocational rehabilitation, employment services, home ownership, and burial.

How To Contact The Department Of Veteran's Affairs

The various benefits available to veterans each has its own specific qualification criteria and potential beneficiaries. In order to determine what benefits you may be entitled to, it is best to contact your local Department of Veteran's Affairs. You can find the office nearest you by looking in the phone book or on the web at www.va.gov. You may also contact the Department by phone at the following numbers:

VA Benefits	1-800-827-1000	Telecommunication Device	
Health Benefits	1-877-222-8387	For the Deaf (TDD)	1-800-829-4833
Education Benefits	1-888-442-4551	CHAMPVA	1-800-733-8387
Life Insurance	1-800-669-8477	Headstones and Markers	1-800-697-6947
Debt Management	1-800-827-0648	Gulf War & Agent Orange	1-800-749-8387
Mammography Hotline	1-888-492-7844	Health Eligibility Center	1-800-929-8387

Documents Needed To Apply For Survivor Benefits

As with Social Security survivor benefits, you will need to apply for Veteran's survivor benefits. You can gather information and apply for certain benefits at the Department of Veteran's Affairs website (www.va.gov). It may be a good idea, however, to apply in person at your local VA office. The items you will need to apply for survivor benefits include:

- A certified copy of the death certificate

- A copy of the certificate of honorable discharge

- Marriage certificate

- Birth certificates of any dependents

- Social Security numbers for you, your children, and the deceased

Medicare / Medicaid

Medicare Insurance

Medicare is a government health insurance plan for people who are 65 or older, or who are disabled, or have permanent kidney failure. The program is administered by the Centers for Medicare and Medicaid Services. The insurance has two parts. Part A is hospital insurance and covers inpatient hospital care and certain follow-up care. You paid for this coverage as part of your Social Security taxes while you were working. Part B is medical insurance and pays for physicians' services and certain other services not covered by Part A. This coverage is optional, and you will be charged a premium for it.

If you are receiving Social Security benefits when you turn 65, Medicare will start automatically. If you are not getting Social Security, you will need to sign up for Medicare close to your 65th birthday, even if you do not plan to retire. You may apply for Medicare by calling the Social Security Administration at 1-800-772-1213 or by visiting your local Social Security office. If you are hearing or speech impaired, you may use the TTY/TDD number at 1-800-325-0778.

There are several publications available that can help you learn more about Medicare eligibility and enrollment and provide guidance in choosing the right plan for you. You may request these publications by calling 1-800-633-4227 (TTY/TDD: 1-877-486-2048). You may also view them online at www.medicare.gov. You will find additional information at the Social Security website (www.ssa.gov) and the Centers for Medicare and Medicaid Services (www.cms.hhs.gov).

Medicaid Insurance

Medicaid is health insurance that helps people who can't afford medical care to pay some or all of their medical bills. It is a state-administered program, and each state sets its own guidelines regarding eligibility and services. Certain services must be covered, however, in order for the states to receive Federal funds. You can find more information about Medicaid by contacting the Centers for Medicare and Medicaid at 1-877-267-2323 (TTY: 1-866-226-1819) or by visiting their website at www.cms.hhs.gov/medicaid/. You can also contact your local public assistance office, where representatives can tell you about your state's eligibility requirements for Medicaid and whether you qualify.

Section 6
What to do After Losing a Spouse or Other Loved One

Even if it has been anticipated, the death of a spouse or other loved one is a very traumatic event. The pain during this time is compounded by a host of legal and financial issues that must be addressed. This section will provide information and instruction that will act as a guide through this difficult time. Items that will be covered in this section include:

Part A – Funeral Arrangements

- ☐ Planning the Funeral
- ☐ Funeral Preferences
- ☐ Obituary Information
- ☐ People To Contact

Part B – Administering the Estate

- ☐ Gathering Information and Documents
- ☐ Transferring Property and Handling Court Proceedings
- ☐ Estate and Trust Duties
- ☐ Tax Reporting
- ☐ Amending Survivor Estate Plans

Part C – Claiming Government Benefits

- ☐ Social Security
- ☐ Veteran's Benefits
- ☐ Medicare / Medicaid

"Immediately after my dad died, Mom and I set her financial affairs in order. Little did we know that just 6 years later she would be diagnosed with Alzheimer's disease. It was a long few years, but because of our advanced planning, I was able to more easily transition into the very difficult task of parenting my parent. Had we not prepared, the additional burden would have made an already difficult situation unbearable."

Kathy H.

Immediately following the death of a spouse, it is important to determine who is responsible for dealing with certain issues. This is important because financial institutions will take instructions only from authorized individuals (for example, the personal representative of an estate, the beneficiary of an insurance policy or retirement account, a trustee, etc.). The surviving spouse often fulfills most of these roles. Have those that are responsible keep a list of activities done, decisions made, and money spent.

PLANNING INSIGHT

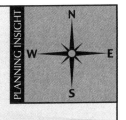

Planning the Funeral

Few people arrange funerals frequently enough to become familiar with all of the planning and decision making involved. This can result in a great deal of stress when it becomes necessary to plan the funeral for a loved one at a time when you are already experiencing tremendous grief and sadness. That is why, there is a growing trend to pre-plan one's funeral. It may be a bit uncomfortable dealing with the subject, but it has many benefits, including making sure your wishes are carried out, covering the costs involved, and most important, relieving your family of having to focus on the details of your death at a time when they should be celebrating your life.

What To Do First

Whether you are pre-planning a funeral or making arrangements after your loved one has died, there are certain steps involved. The first step is to contact the funeral director. The funeral director's job is to inform you of your options and help you plan an appropriate service. Make sure to give him an idea of the amount of money you have budgeted for the funeral. This will help him to make recommendations that will fit within your budget. Once you have your options before you and a budget determined, you can make the final decisions concerning the service. Some examples of the decisions you will need to make include:

- Burial or cremation
- Time/Day of service
- Casket
- Pallbearers
- Clothing

- Music
- Flowers
- Food
- Location of service
  (church or mortuary)

There are worksheets on the following pages that will help you and your spouse to record your wishes concerning these things.

Most people will pay for their funeral when they do the pre-planning. This guarantees that the costs will be covered and relieves your loved ones from having to pay for the funeral after you have died.

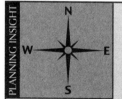

PLANNING INSIGHT

In 1984, the Federal Trade Commission (FTC) issued rules concerning funeral industry practices and pricing structure. This "Funeral Rule" says that every funeral home must provide a General Price List, which gives detailed prices for its goods and services. By calling different funeral homes and requesting their price lists, you can more easily compare prices among different providers. Another important aspect of the rule requires funeral providers to give you a Statement of Funerals and Services Selected after you have made the decisions concerning your funeral. The statement gives you a breakdown of the prices for individual items you are considering for purchase, as well as an overall price for the funeral.

Funeral Preferences

If you need additional space to record your preferences, there is a "notes" section beginning on page 117.

Your funeral preferences	
Funeral home preference	
Address	
Telephone number	
Description of pre-arrangements	
Location of pre-arrangement documents	
Burial or cremation	
Viewing wishes (open or closed casket)	
Location of the service	
Clergyperson	
Other speakers	
Content of the service	
Hymns/songs	
Memorials to	
Pallbearers (typically 6)	
Service indoors, graveside, or both	
Cemetery	
City/state	
Legal description of plot	
Location of plot deeds	
Special requests (biblical passages, clothing, etc.)	
Casket (steel, hardwood, copper, bronze, etc.)	
What to do with ashes if cremated	

Your spouse's funeral preferences

Funeral home preference	
Address	
Telephone number	
Description of pre-arrangements	
Location of pre-arrangement documents	
Burial or cremation	
Viewing wishes (open or closed casket)	
Location of the service	
Clergyperson	
Other speakers	
Content of the service	
Hymns/songs	
Memorials to	
Pallbearers (typically 6)	
Service indoors, graveside, or both	
Cemetery	
City/state	
Legal description of plot	
Location of plot deeds	
Special requests (biblical passages, clothing, etc.)	
Casket (steel, hardwood, copper, bronze, etc.)	
What to do with ashes if cremated	

Obituary Information

As with most decisions relating to the death of a loved one, it is much easier to have obituary information taken care of prior to a person's death. This section will give you an outline of the information typically listed in an obituary and will provide space for both you and your spouse to record information that you would like included.

Again, if you need additional space, the notes section begins on page 117.

Your obituary information	
Full name	
Marital status	
Address	
Date of birth	
Place of birth	
Citizenship	
Spouse's name	
Children's names	
Father's name	
Mother's name	
Employer	
Religious affiliations	
Undergraduate degree/school/date received	
Graduate degree/school/date received	
Professional memberships and designations	
Other organizational memberships	
Volunteer work	
Special honors or awards	
Details of military service	

Your spouse's obituary information

Full name	
Marital status	
Address	
Date of birth	
Place of birth	
Citizenship	
Spouse's name	
Children's names	
Father's name	
Mother's name	
Employer	
Religious affiliations	
Undergraduate degree/school/date received	
Graduate degree/school/date received	
Professional memberships and designations	
Other organizational memberships	
Volunteer work	
Special honors or awards	
Details of military service	

People to Contact

It is important to contact certain people if your spouse or other loved ones pass away. We mentioned earlier that you should contact the funeral director. Others you should contact include:

- [ ] Family, friends, and relatives
- [ ] The personal representative named in your spouse's will and/or trustee of their trust
- [ ] Anyone that has power of attorney for your spouse, to inform them that it is no longer valid
- [ ] Your spouse's employer. Make sure to ask them about any wages due, unpaid vacation time, sick pay, and death or retirement benefits. Contact information is on page 14 of this workbook
- [ ] Your financial adviser. Don't make any rushed decisions, but begin discussing your different options
- [ ] Your attorney. Have him/her walk you through any will or trust documents and clearly explain the process of settling the estate
- [ ] Your insurance agent. Professional advisers are listed beginning on page 15. A list of policies and where they are located is listed on page 58. Talk to your agent about your different options and begin filling out the necessary claim forms
- [ ] The bank. Bank accounts and contact information are listed on page 22
- [ ] Credit card companies. This information is listed on page 49
- [ ] Any clubs, professional associations, or fraternal organizations
- [ ] The Social Security Administration. As discussed on page 92, you may be entitled to receive survivor's benefits
- [ ] Notify the state office for inheritance tax. Many states require a release from this office before certain benefits can be paid

The contact information for many of the people listed above has been recorded earlier in this workbook. In the space provided below, record the contact information for anyone that you would like to be contacted in the event of your death whose information does not already appear in this workbook.

Name	Address	Phone number

Gathering Information and Documents

The first step in handling an estate is to schedule a meeting between family members and advisers to gather and update family and financial information and to collect the documents needed to administer the estate. By providing advisers with a copy of this workbook, you will be off to a good start and save a great deal of time and expense. At this meeting, family and advisers should review the estate plan documents to determine which phases of the estate administration process are required and decide who will be responsible for performing the various tasks.

In order to file for certain benefits and to finalize a deceased's estate, you will need to collect certain papers. Most of them are listed below:

☐ Death Certificates

You can purchase certified copies of the death certificate either directly from the county health department or from your funeral director. Many of the offices and agencies you will be working with to settle an estate will require a copy of the death certificate; therefore, it is important to get multiple certified copies (usually 10).

☐ Insurance Policies

The locations of your insurance policies are recorded in Section 3 of this workbook. Having the policies available will make communication easier when you contact the insurance companies regarding benefits.

☐ Social Security Numbers and Cards

There is space provided in Section 8 of this workbook to record the location of your Social Security cards. You will need these numbers when applying for certain benefits.

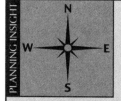

Losing a loved one marks the beginning of a difficult process known as estate administration. As we grieve a loss, we are also called upon to follow the wishes of our loved one, as expressed through his or her estate planning, and in accordance with the Federal and state laws. The steps involved in handling an estate include: 1) Gathering information and documents 2) transfer of property and court proceedings 3) estate and trust duties 4) tax reporting and 5) survivor estate plans. These tasks are usually performed by the people designated in our estate planning documents, with the help of family and advisers.

☐ Military Discharge Papers

If your spouse was a veteran, you will need a copy of his or her certificate of discharge. The location of those documents is listed in Section 8 of this workbook. If you can't find a copy of the discharge certificate, you may request a copy by writing to:

> The Department of Defense
> National Personnel Record Center
> 9700 Page Avenue
> St. Louis, MO 63132

☐ Marriage Certificate

You will need copies of your marriage certificate if you are going to apply for benefits based on your marital relationship. The location of your marriage certificate should be listed in Section 8. If you cannot find a copy, you may obtain one at the office of the County Clerk where the marriage license was issued.

☐ Prenuptial Agreements

Certain rights to inherit property may be affected by prenuptial agreements. Please provide the estate attorney with a copy of any such agreement.

☐ Children's Birth Certificates

If you are applying for Social Security benefits for dependent children, you will need copies of their birth certificates. Section 8 lists where they are located. If you cannot find the copies, you may obtain them at either the state or county public health offices where the children were born.

☐ Original Will and/or Trust

The location of your wills and trusts are located in Section 4. You will need the original signed documents to arrange for the correct division and distribution of property.

☐ List of Assets

A list of assets is in Section 2 of this workbook. This list will help you as you dispose of property and re-title assets.

☐ Income and Gift Tax Returns

Collect at least the last two income tax returns and any gift tax returns filed by the deceased.

Transferring Property and Handling Court Precedings

It is a good rule of thumb to avoid making big decisions shortly after losing a loved one. You should postpone those decisions, whenever possible, until you have had a chance to deal with your grief and gain a better understanding of how your life will change. Too often, a grieving widow or widower will give away belongings or relocate, only to regret those actions later. Decisions you should make fairly quickly (usually within 6 months), however, relate to transferring property, claiming survivor benefits, and re-titling of assets.

Receiving benefits could include receiving a payout on a life insurance policy or deciding what to do with IRAs or 401(k)s where you are listed as the beneficiary. Re-titling of assets typically includes changing the registrations on vehicles, residences, stocks, bonds, investments, and savings and checking accounts. The process for re-titling assets varies from state to state and institution to institution. Depending on the type of asset, however, there are certain documents that you will almost always need:

- A certified copy of the death certificate. As mentioned earlier in this section, it is usually a good idea to have multiple copies on hand.

- A notarized Affidavit of Domicile.

- A complete copy of any trust documents.

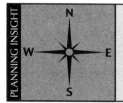

PLANNING INSIGHT

If you are the beneficiary of both life insurance and retirement plan assets, it is usually a good idea to claim the insurance benefits first. Insurance benefits are typically income tax-free, and the payment choices and benefit processing are usually simpler than those with retirement plan assets.

The process of transferring property, claiming benefits, and re-titling assets has specific rules and regulations that you will need to follow. You should work closely with your advisers throughout this process in order to make decisions appropriate for your specific situation. The following discussions will cover the different methods available to transfer assets from a deceased person to his or her living beneficiaries, and how to go about handling the transfer.

☐ Will

Section 4 of this workbook includes the details and location of your loved one's will. The will conveys property held in a deceased person's name alone to the heirs named in the will. If your loved one used a will to transfer property, the estate attorney may need to assist by opening a probate court proceeding in the county court to validate the will, notify any creditors, transfer title of property, and determine any inheritance taxes. By reviewing a complete list of assets and how they were titled, the estate attorney will be able to tell you if a probate is necessary and review with you the steps and expense involved.

Joint Tenancy With Right of Survivorship

Section 2 of this workbook should list any property held in joint tenancy. Joint tenancy property passes directly to the surviving joint tenant. The surviving joint tenant automatically becomes the owner of the entire property. The surviving joint tenant should take steps to clear the deceased person's name from the title of the property by contacting the financial institution involved with the property. Work with the estate attorney to clear the title to real estate held in joint tenancy.

☐ "Payable On Death" Or "Transfer On Death" Designation

Section 2 should list any accounts held with a "Payable on Death" or "Transfer on Death" designation. P.O.D. and T.O.D. accounts, normally bank accounts or brokerage accounts, pass directly to beneficiaries based upon a beneficiary designation form that the deceased person completed and filed with the financial institution holding the account. The beneficiary should work with the deceased person's financial adviser to arrange for transfer of the account.

☐ Beneficiary Designations

Sections 2 and 3 should list assets and life insurance, along with beneficiary designations. Property with beneficiary designations passes directly to the named beneficiary based upon the beneficiary designation form completed by the deceased person. The beneficiary of the policy or account should work with the deceased person's life insurance and financial advisers to contact the financial institution to claim a death benefit or have the retirement account transferred.

☐ Revocable Living Trust

Section 4 of this workbook should list the details and location of any revocable living trusts left by your loved one. As discussed in that section, property titled to a revocable living trust is held for or distributed to beneficiaries by the trustee in accordance with the provisions of the trust document. The trustee of any revocable trust left by the deceased person should work with the estate attorney, financial adviser, and accountant to arrange for the division, distribution, or ongoing management of any trusts.

☐ Intestacy

If, for any property, the deceased person did not arrange for the use of one of the methods described above, the estate may face intestacy. Each state has specific laws regarding the passing of property when a deceased person has not left instructions. The estate attorney will need to assist in opening an intestacy proceeding in the county court to pass the property to the heirs in accordance with the laws of the state of the decedent's residence.

Estate and Trust Duties

During administration of an estate, certain duties must be carried out by the personal representative designated under the will, or the trustee designated in any trusts, or the estate beneficiaries, depending upon how certain property is titled. The successor trustee and/or personal representative step into the role of manager of the trust or estate property and take on responsibility for the protection and distribution of property owned by the estate or trust. Family members should meet with the advisers listed in Section 1 to discuss who should be responsible for each of these tasks:

☐ Collect, Safeguard, Liquidate, and
Manage Estate Property for Beneficiaries

Responsibility for the management of property will fall to the trustee if the property is titled to a trust, or to the personal representative if the property is passing by will.

☐ Account for Receipts and Disbursements

Any bills that are the obligation of the deceased should generally be paid by the estate. It is important for the personal representative and/or trustee to keep detailed records of bills paid or money received. This information will be used by the accountant to complete tax returns for the deceased and will be needed to prepare a complete report to satisfy beneficiaries. Bills that are the obligation of both spouses should be paid by the surviving spouse in order to keep a good credit rating. It is a good idea to contact the different billing entities to have the deceased person's name removed from the account. Any credit cards held exclusively in the name of the deceased person should be paid by the estate and cancelled. For cards held jointly, pay those bills, then contact the credit card company and have them issue you a new card in your name only.

☐ Plan for Continuation of a Family Business

The details of any family business owned by the deceased person should be listed on page 40. The personal representative and/or trustee should work closely with advisers and family to plan for continuation of the business. Collect and review with advisers any shareholder or buy/sell agreements that may relate to the operation of the business.

☐ Communicate With and Report to Family Beneficiaries

Most problems associated with handling an estate begin with a lack of effective communication. The personal representative and/or trustee, as well as advisers, should communicate regularly with family and other beneficiaries to keep them up to date. Beneficiaries should also receive periodic reports that include an inventory of the estate property and financial information regarding income and expenses of the estate.

Tax Reporting

There are several tax issues related to estates that the personal representative and/or trustee need to be aware of. Family members should consult with the accountant, estate attorney, and financial advisers to identify which tax returns will be required and who will take responsibility for preparing those returns. These advisers will help you take advantage of all available tax-saving opportunities and will assist you in navigating the complex web of tax rules.

☐ Federal and State Income Tax Returns

Final Federal and state income tax returns will be due on April 15 of the year following the year of death. The estate and any ongoing trusts may be required to file a tax return each year until they are terminated.

☐ Federal Estate Tax Returns

If the value of the estate exceeds certain limits, a Federal estate tax return will be due 9 months after the date of death. As you complete an inventory of the estate and pay any final expenses, the estate attorney will be able to estimate the amount of tax, if any, which will be due.

☐ State Estate and Inheritance Tax Returns

Many states require the filing of estate and/or inheritance tax returns. Similar to the Federal estate tax, as you gather further information about the assets and expenses of the estate, the estate attorney will be able to estimate the amount of tax, if any, which will be due.

Below we have included a table of significant tax reporting dates. As you work with your advisers, fill in the dates and persons responsible for filing any returns required.

Tax reporting dates		
Type of tax	Tax preparer	Due date
Deceased's Federal and state income tax returns		
Trust and/or estate income tax returns		
State or county inheritance tax		
State estate tax		
Federal estate tax (9 months from death)		

Amending Survivor Estate Plans

The death of a loved one always affects the planning of other family members. When a loved one passes away, the surviving spouse, children, and other beneficiaries should meet with their estate planning attorney and financial advisers to update their estate plan documents and coordinate inherited property with their own estate and financial plans.

Applying For Government Benefits

In Section 5 of this workbook, there is an extensive discussion on government benefits. As a widow or widower, you may be entitled to receive benefits from one of those governmental organizations. By reviewing Section 5, you will be able to determine which of those benefits you may be entitled to and how to go about applying for them. Please reference the following pages for further information:

Section 7
Safe-Deposit Box Storage

People will often rent a safe-deposit box at a bank in order to store important documents, expensive jewelry, or other valuables. Federal and state laws typically do not address what can and cannot be held in a safe-deposit box. Banks, however, will often put restrictions into the contract that you sign with them when you rent a box. Common restrictions include explosives, firearms, and drug paraphernalia. Just because an item isn't on the "restriction" list, however, doesn't necessarily mean that it is a good idea to store it in your box. Below is a list of items that you should and should not keep in your safe-deposit box:

Items you should keep in your safe-deposit box:

- Originals of birth, marriage and death certificates
- Adoption papers
- Citizenship records
- Military service records
- Vehicle titles
- Real estate deeds
- Mortgage paperwork
- Stock and bond certificates
- Certificates of deposit
- Precious metals
- Valuable collectables
- Jewelry
- Photographs, video and/or a written inventory of your home's contents

As a general rule, do not keep anything in your safe-deposit box that you may need in an emergency, such as a power of attorney. Since the safe-deposit box of a deceased person is often sealed at the time of death, do not keep items in your box that your heirs or personal representatives may need right away. Items you should not keep in your safe-deposit box include:

- Will or estate plan (you may keep a copy here, but make sure to have another copy elsewhere)
- Life insurance policies (instead, put a list of your policies)
- Medical or financial powers of attorney
- Burial instructions
- Cemetery deeds
- Funeral arrangements
- Property owned by others

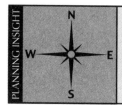

PLANNING INSIGHT

Items you store in a safe-deposit box are generally not insured by the bank. Your homeowner's insurance policy may provide some coverage, but it is usually limited. Speak to your insurance agent about adding a rider to your policy that will cover the valuables in your safe-deposit box in the unlikely event that they are stolen or damaged in a fire or flood.

In the space below, make a list of items stored in your safe-deposit box:

Name of bank	Address of bank	Phone number

Name(s) of person(s) authorized to access box

Safe-deposit box contents

Document Locator System

This section lists the location of important documents and other items. If a particular item has been previously discussed in this workbook, the page number of that discussion is listed. There is also a space next to each item to write its location. This will help to give you a consolidated list that will act as a quick and easy reference.

Knowing what to keep and what to throw away can be the difference between an organized filing system and an overstuffed filing cabinet. In case there is a billing dispute, it is usually a good idea to hang onto bills for about a year. You should generally keep your tax returns and other tax-related items for a period of six years. Keep items related to the purchase of stocks, real estate, and other assets for as long as you own them. Most types of identity documents, wills, and insurance policies should be kept indefinitely. Identity theft is one of the fastest growing crimes in the U.S. When you do dispose of certain documents, make sure to shred them prior to throwing them away.

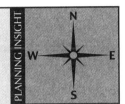

PLANNING INSIGHT

Identity Documents

- ☐ Social Security card(s) _____
- ☐ Birth certificate(s) _____
- ☐ Citizenship papers _____
- ☐ Adoption papers _____
- ☐ Military discharge papers _____
- ☐ Marriage certificate _____
- ☐ Children's birth certificates _____
- ☐ Children's adoption papers _____
- ☐ Divorce/separation papers _____
- ☐ Passport _____

Asset-Related Documents

- ☐ Checking records — Pages 22-23
- ☐ Savings records — Pages 22-23
- ☐ Investment accounts — Pages 24-37
- ☐ Titles and deeds to real estate — Pages 38-39
- ☐ Time share agreements _____
- ☐ Stock certificates _____
- ☐ Bond certificates _____
- ☐ Auto ownership records — Pages 41-42
- ☐ Boat ownership records — Pages 41-42

Liability-Related Documents

☐ List of credit cards   Page 49

☐ Debt notes   Pages 47-53

☐ Loan agreements   Pages 47-53

Insurance Documents

☐ Life insurance policies   Page 58

☐ Health insurance policies   Pages 60-61

☐ Disability insurance policies   Page 63

☐ Long-term care insurance policies   Page 66

☐ Homeowner's insurance policies   Page 68

☐ Auto insurance policies   Page 75

☐ Dental insurance policies   Page 77

☐ Umbrella insurance policies   Page 78

☐ Renter's insurance policies   Page 79

Estate Planning Documents

☐ Will(s)   Page 87

☐ Trust(s)   Pages 89-90

☐ Powers of attorney   Pages 83 and 85

Funeral Documents

☐ Burial instructions   Pages 99-100

☐ Cemetery plot deed(s)   Pages 99-100

Miscellaneous Documents

☐ Employment contracts   _____

☐ Business agreements   _____

☐ Tax returns   _____

☐ Safe combination   _____

☐ Computer passwords   _____

☐ Safe-deposit box keys   _____

☐ Professional membership list   Pages 101-102

☐ Fraternal/civic membership list   Pages 101-102

☐ List of advisers   Pages 15-19

Annual Review Checklist

It is a good idea to review and update the information in this book at least once a year to make sure that it portrays an up-to-date, accurate picture of your circumstances. Below is a simple list of questions that you can ask yourself periodically. If you answer "yes" to any of the questions, that is a red flag that the current information you have recorded in this workbook may need to be updated. Following each question are lists of items that you should check on as a result of that particular life change.

1. Has my or any of my family members' marital status changed? If so:

- Review the beneficiary designations on your investment accounts and insurance policies.
- Meet with your attorney and make any necessary changes to your estate plan documents.
- Consider updating the titling on your accounts and other assets (checking account, credit cards, automobiles, investment accounts, house, etc.).
- Review your insurance coverage to ensure that it is still adequate.

2. Has a child or grandchild been born, adopted, or become related by marriage? If so:

- Speak with your financial adviser about college planning.
- Review the beneficiary designations on your investment accounts and insurance policies.
- Meet with your attorney and make any necessary changes to your estate plan documents.
- Review your insurance coverage to ensure that it is still adequate.

3. Has my or my spouse's health changed significantly? If so:

- Review your health insurance coverage. If you have an illness that requires doctors visits or hospitalization, check with your provider to make sure that you have gotten the appropriate referrals and that you are using care facilities that are covered by your plan.

- Review your health care power of attorney, so that your spouse (or other person you choose) can make medical decisions on your behalf if you become incapacitated.

- Meet with your attorney to make sure that your estate plan documents are up to date, and that your assets have been titled correctly.

4) Has there been a significant change in any other family member's health, or have I had a family member pass away? If so:

- Meet with your attorney and make any necessary changes to your will and estate plan documents.

- If you are providing special care for a child or relative, make sure that you arrange for someone else to care for that person, should something happen to you. This includes providing that person with both written instructions and appropriate resources. If necessary, meet with your insurance agent to make sure you have enough insurance to accomplish this.

5. Have you acquired or divested yourself of any business? If so:

• If you purchased a business, meet with your insurance agent to ensure that you have proper coverage.

• Update your asset and liability section to reflect the new business.

• Since it is a non-liquid asset, make sure that there are instructions on what to do with the business should something happen to you. Make sure that, if necessary, there is both insurance and the proper buy-sell arrangement in place to allow your partner(s) or key employee(s) to buy out your spouse should something happen to you.

6. Have the values of any of your assets changed significantly? Have you acquired or sold any real estate? If so:

• Update your net worth figures. Meet with your financial adviser and make sure that you are still on track to accomplish your goals.

7. Have you changed jobs? If so:

• Make sure you update the information in your workbook to include your new employee benefits and employer contact information.

8. Have you made changes to any part of your insurance coverage? If so:

• Update the insurance section of this workbook.

• Review your beneficiary information and make any appropriate changes.

9. Have you changed your mind about whom you would like to have act as guardians, executors, and/or trustees, as pertains to your financial, legal, or family affairs? If so:

• Meet with your attorney in order to make the appropriate changes to your will, trust, and/or powers of attorney.

• Meet with your insurance agent to make sure that your policies have the appropriate beneficiaries.

10. Do you have any significant projects underway (building project, business campaign, charitable endeavor)? If so:

• Make sure that you include a detailed explanation of what you would want done with the project should something happen to you. In addition, make sure you have someone who could take your place if necessary.

Section 10
Notes

Use this section if you need additional space to record details or preferences from previous sections. You may also use it to write a note or special instructions to your family.

www.ifsomethinghappenstome.com

www.ifsomethinghappenstome.com